4 Lobes 66

You
AND YOUR
Brain

You
AND YOUR
Brain

by Judith Groch
ILLUSTRATED BY E. L. SISLEY

Foreword by Clark H. Millikan, M.D.,
of the Mayo Clinic

HARPER & ROW, PUBLISHERS
NEW YORK, EVANSTON, AND LONDON

YOU AND YOUR BRAIN

To the memory of Sigmund Noel Groch, M.D.

CONTENTS

ACKNOWLEDGMENTS

I wish to express my deep gratitude to Dr. Clark H. Millikan, Professor of Neurology, Mayo Foundation Graduate School, University of Minnesota, and to Dr. Eli Goldstein, Professor of Clinical Medicine, New York Medical College, whose devoted interest and constructive criticism have helped to make this book a more useful and readable work. Dr. Millikan read and criticized the entire manuscript, bringing to the task not only his extensive professional knowledge but his profound respect for the rights and dignity of the general reader. Dr. Goldstein, with rare editorial vigilance, reviewed the manuscript, attending meticulously to matters of clarity, accuracy, and style.

For his encouragement and guidance and for his kindness in making available to me books from his personal library, I am deeply indebted to Dr. Raymond D. Adams, Bullard Professor of Neurology, Harvard Medical School, and Chief of Neurology Service, Massachusetts General Hospital. I also wish to express my appreciation to Dr. Ellen McDevitt, Dr. Fletcher McDowell, Dr. Harold Samelson, Dr. Harry L. Shapiro, and Mr. Gerald Weiss for advice and assistance in their special fields; and to my editor, Miss Janet Loranger, for her valuable suggestions and critical judgment. I claim as my own responsibility, however, any errors of fact or interpretation which may remain.

Finally, I wish to thank my loyal friend Miss Kathleen Monahan for typing the manuscript, and my family for their patience and understanding and for the many times they have generously adjusted their needs to suit mine.

J. G.

New York City
May, 1963

FOREWORD

"Dad, where can I find out something about the nervous system—but not in one of your medical books?" This is something I have heard from my own children, at ages ten to seventeen, and in these times of emphasis on education, science, electronics in general, and computers in particular, it is the kind of question hundreds of young people must ask every day.

When the author began plans for this book, the need for a comprehensive volume for young readers about the brain and nervous system was obvious. However, it seemed to me an ambitious undertaking for one not formally trained in anatomy, physiology, and medicine. Judith Groch's book has dispelled my doubts. Herein the nervous system of man is reconstructed and its anatomy made exciting and meaningful as the description of neural function unfolds. The reader sees the nerve impulse on its way, finds out about reflexes, motor function, sensations, the autonomic nervous system, and the loci of language. There are fascinating portrayals of such entities as consciousness, memory, intellect, and motivation. Finally, the author provides a thought-provoking discussion of man's brain and its synthetic image, the modern computer.

This is a serious book—and an accurate one. The author must have studied prodigiously, and her writing not only brings facts to life but does so with clarity.

"Men must be taught as if you taught them not." There has long been a need for a book which describes the nervous system in a way as fascinating as the nervous system is in fact, outside the coldly intellectual domain of the scientist's textbook. The need is fulfilled here with dignity and charm.

—*Clark H. Millikan, M.D.*
Professor of Neurology, Mayo Foundation,
Graduate School, University of Minnesota,
and Consultant in Neurology,
Mayo Clinic, Rochester, Minnesota

You
AND YOUR
Brain

1

SO NEAR AND YET SO FAR

The sleek machine standing in the austere, air-conditioned laboratory looks somewhat like a streamlined kitchen cabinet. Its front panels, however, open to reveal a colorful jungle of wires woven in unbelievably intricate patterns like the enchanted basketwork of some inspired weaver. This incredible maze of wiring is not a sorcerer's handiwork, but the "mind" of IBM's amazing highspeed computer which bears the unglamorous name 7094.

The 7094 can add two numbers containing 36 pieces of information approximately every four millionths of a second. It can multiply two numbers of the same size in four to ten millionths of a second. And in a few minutes it can solve an equation which would take an ordinary man using a desk calculator many hundreds of years to complete.

The concept of such astronomical speed is almost too much for our minds to grasp, but it is even more remarkable that man's brain can design and build an electronic wizard which can memorize a billion pieces of information or review the entire history of a star's life—yet man does not know how his *own* brain remembers that 2 + 2 = 4.

Today, by means of the ingenious tools and machines he has created, man is planning to leave his ancestral planet behind and journey forth beyond day and night to a rendezvous with the moon. In time, we are told, the moon will be little more than a harbor in the sky from which to launch voyages to other worlds in our solar system. But what do we know about the brain which not only designs space ships, but long before the dawn of the space age dreamed of exploring the lunar mountains and of scooping up precious particles of moon dust? It is no different from the brain which conceived and designed the ships that sailed down the ancient Nile. It is no different from the brain which twenty-five to thirty thousand years ago discovered how to make fire by striking a flint against a piece of iron pyrite. The truth is, we still know too little about the human brain. Not in the paths which lead beyond the far side of the moon, but within our silent skulls lies the deepest mystery known to man.

Yet we take our brains for granted. In ancient times men thought that the heart was the source of courage and that cowardice dwelt in the liver. Even today we say, "I love you with all my heart," when in truth the heart is a muscular pump with a full-time job of servicing the body with blood. Love remains the brain's affair.

We rarely notice the remarkable role our brain plays in conducting the events of our daily life. We expect to breathe, tie our shoe laces, drive automobiles, and plan next summer's vacation. Nobody is impressed by the acrobatics of such a seemingly simple action as standing. Yet the brain must adjust the tensions of two hundred pairs of muscles in order to make this single feat possible. We consider it our birthright that we shall walk and speak and remember where we live. Stranger still, when we go to sleep and wake up again, we are never surprised.

The human brain is a spongy mass of pinkish-gray tissue which weighs about three pounds and is crammed into a bony cave at the top of the head. Neurologists estimate that the entire brain contains roughly thirteen billion nerve cells, and yet, remarkably, the living brain is insensitive to touch, to heat, even to the surgeon's knife. By means of a network of nerves which travel from the brain to every part of the body, this master organ keeps the body running, coordinates all its near and far outposts, and ultimately makes it possible for us to think, plan, design space ships—in fact, to be human beings.

The brain is an incredibly complex organ and does not easily surrender its secrets. But scientists are remarkably persistent and remain undaunted by the fact that for every answer they find they must face a new chain of problems.

We already know many things about the basic unit

of the brain and nervous system—the nerve cell. Although other cells in the body can be replaced, we are born with all the nerve cells we shall ever possess. Every nerve cell operates like every other nerve cell. The nerve cells of a mouse are not much smaller than ours, and as far as we know, nerve cells do not move around in the brain as a result of experience and learning. Then how does the nerve cell perform all the gymnastics of human thinking? We do not know.

And what about intelligence and the quality of thinking? Are bigger brains better brains? Certainly an outstanding factor in the evolution of man from lower animals has been the increase in the size of man's brain relative to the size of his body. Since the brain fairly well fills the skull cavity, scientists generally measure brain size by giving the cranial capacity. In the case of fossil skulls this is the only possible method, for the soft tissues of the actual brain have long since disappeared. The human brain is, on the average, 1400 cubic centimeters in volume. The brain of the modern ape varies between 325 and 650 cubic centimeters, and the man-apes who roamed the earth a million years ago had brains ranging from 450 to 850 cubic centimeters.

Nevertheless the success with which a brain thinks cannot be credited to its weight alone. At birth the human brain weighs about the same as that of a fully grown chimpanzee. Yet the ape spends his day swinging up and down the branches of a tree, or if he is a scientific chimpanzee he may be willing to solve simple problems in banana retrieving for his human friends in the laboratory. The human baby with the same size brain is helpless. His tiny arms and legs jerk in unco-ordinated movements, and he can barely see the rails of his crib; in fact, he depends entirely upon his mother to feed him and keep him alive. In time, however, the baby will grow up to speak and write, to contemplate atoms and apes, and to take a conscious hand in chart-ing his own destiny. What makes these brains differ-ent? We can only speculate.

Even in adult human beings the absolute weight of the brain is so variable that it is not a reliable guide to intelligence. The brain of Anatole France, the brilliant French writer, measured only 1100 cubic centimeters —somewhat below average. The brains of two other great writers, Jonathan Swift and Ivan Turgenev, were about 2000 cubic centimeters in volume. And one of the largest human brains ever measured belonged to an idiot. Female brains weigh a few ounces less than male brains, but this is in proportion to women's smaller body weight. The brain of a genius, however, does not differ in appearance from the brain of an ordinary man, and even with the aid of a microscope no one, thus far, has been able to demonstrate a differ-ence in the basic structure of average and exceptional brains. Then what is the explanation for superior in-telligence? Today scientists suspect that the answer may be hidden in the submicroscopic structure of the brain cells and that rather than the number of cells, it may be the way in which the brain *uses* its resources which is significant. If we knew the answer to this question, we would be closer to the discovery of the brain's most tightly kept secret—how we think.

Within its three-pound mass of tangled cells the brain holds other secrets which are as deep as the mystery of life itself. We spend one third of our lives asleep, and yet we do not know what sleep is. Consciousness, of which sleep is only one aspect, is an ancient realm, vast and unexplored. At this moment you are reading a book about your brain. Although you cannot see it, you are aware that you have a brain; your dog has a brain, but he is not aware of it. Is the dog's head filled with emptiness? Until your attention was drawn to it, you were not particularly conscious of the fact that you were reading, nor did you notice the steady pressure against your thighs produced by the chair on which you are sitting. If you are bored, you may fall asleep while reading and you will sleep through a thunderstorm but awaken suddenly if your dog whines. Why? We are not certain. The mechanisms of consciousness and of all the subtle levels of awareness which fall between "being conscious" and "being unconscious" still remain to be discovered.

And what about memory? Despite all the psychological studies of how memories are formed, we still do not know what changes take place *in the brain* when a memory is established. If you could look into a working brain, you naturally would not expect to find the song you recently learned or a notation about next week's dental appointment. But it might be reasonable to suppose that memories are stored in code form within the individual nerve cells of the brain. Even a quick look at the mechanisms of the nerve cell will illustrate the difficulties scientists must overcome if they are to solve the riddle of memory.

Like all cells in the body, the nerve cell is made of a substance called *protoplasm,* which is the raw material of life. Protoplasm in turn consists of submicroscopic units called *molecules.* The life of the tiny molecule is brief, and from time to time it burns out and is replaced, so that in a sense today's nerve cell is not yesterday's nerve cell. It has been estimated that every seven years there is a complete turnover of *all* the molecules in the body. It therefore seems a contradiction to think of memory as something permanently etched into the core of the nerve cell, for despite the constant replacement of its basic matter each nerve cell continues to know all that it needs to know to be part of YOU. Recently scientists have found a clue to how the nerve cell may accomplish this seemingly impossible feat.

There are other questions we may ask. What is imagination? How do we know who we are? How does an idea trigger a set of nerve impulses which, in turn, make you lift your arm? What happens inside the brain when it is sick? How do we learn?

Many evenings as I prepared the material for this chapter, I found myself drifting from my subject, the brain, to wander deep into the fascinating lives of electronic computers. The intricate details of computer structure and function by no means provide easy reading, but I soon realized that compared to the infinite mysteries of the living brain, computers are a logical and relaxing subject. No matter how remarkable and intricate the computer may be, man made the computer, and so he knows what he put into it and how it functions. Exploring the living brain, however, proves to be a different kind of venture and makes enormous demands of our own brain. Fortunately the brain is the most flexible and adaptable organ in the body, and an examination of itself is inevitably the challenge the human brain must accept.

Because it is the bodily organ of the mind, the brain promises exciting study—perhaps even romantic and mysterious adventures. By comparison, it may seem to us at times that those more primitive areas of the brain, which are concerned with processes essential to life and which we share with many creatures much lower on the evolutionary scale, are quite unexciting. But we must never forget, as we consider man's unique heritage, that unless the regions of the brain which operate our vital mechanisms function properly, man's glorious mind may be of little use to him.

Surgeons have shown that we can manage reasonably well without part of the brain territory in which our thoughts are processed. But even a small tumor in one of the ancient but vital centers may produce such a complicated breakdown in the function of the body that the individual is left quite helpless, perhaps even in mortal danger. A person who cannot control his arm well enough to bring his food to his mouth, whose vision is blurred, and whose breathing is in danger of stopping has little use for even the most splendid mind. Man can be man only when he has a brain to run his body for him. As for the brain—it functions as a whole and no single part can claim all the glory.

One would think, then, that on a rainy afternoon, when the heavens do not beckon and a walk on the ocean floor seems uninviting, the stay-at-home scientist would turn to the convenient problem waiting right inside his head. Yet the lands hidden two thousand fathoms below the surface of the sea and the worlds which spin through space are more accessible than the brain each of us carries locked in his skull.

There are many reasons for this. The human brain is the most complicated mechanism in the world. It is made of billions of parts which are directly or potentially connected with each other. All the telephone, telegraph, radio, and radar apparatus in the world is less intricate than the three pounds of brain within our skulls. Furthermore, the duties of this tight knot of nerve cells, about the size of an average grapefruit, range from keeping our blood vessels from collapsing to playing chess.

A most important area of brain research is the study of diseased or injured brains. We know, for example, that injury to a certain part of the brain paralyzes the right hand; in another region injury results in blindness; damage to still a different area leaves the victim unable to utter words although he can write and understand them. Bit by bit, with endless patience, scientists have succeeded in mapping various regions of the brain. The task is not as simple as it looks, and at present many boundaries remain ill-defined, for despite the fact that certain parts of the brain seem to be charged with specific duties, the cells of the brain are so endlessly interconnected that activity in one area always involves other sections of the brain. Finally, we must understand that maps of the brain's territory, exploration of its communication routes, even studies of how human beings behave, still do not tell us *how* the brain functions or, in other words, what happens within your nerve cells when you awaken and "see" the sun glittering in the morning sky and your "heart skips with joy."

The living brain is not a willing performer. It is silent and folded in on itself. We cannot feel it as we do our beating heart, nor is any movement visible on an X-ray film. Yet the brain has a language of its own —electricity. Nerve cells constantly send out electrical charges, and by studying these rhythms, sometimes called brain waves, we are beginning to learn something about the working habits of nerve cells. Brain waves were first studied in 1929 by Dr. Hans Berger in Germany. Using standard radio equipment he amplified the electrical patterns of the brain coming through the scalp. The brain-wave record is called an *electroencephalogram* (EEG), and its patterns tend to be characteristic for each individual, very much the way fingerprints identify their owners. The EEG indicates whether the subject's eyes are open or closed and varies according to a great many other conditions, such as age, emotional state, disease, attention, and blood sugar level. However, placing electrodes on the scalp or even on the exposed brain is a technique with certain limitations. It is somewhat like placing a microphone outside a house. The microphone picks up the sounds of household activity, but it is difficult to tell which sounds are coming from the living room and which from the kitchen. A rumpus in the front hall may drown out quiet sounds in the rear bedroom.

And so, as is true in much scientific research, we must rely on experimental animals to substitute for us. But as a laboratory subject the animal is in certain ways seriously inadequate. Physiologically the ape's heart and the dog's heart are not too different from ours. But for all its fascinating structural similarity the chimpanzee's brain is not a human brain. It is smaller, and furthermore the frontal lobes, the seat of many of our higher mental functions, are in the ape proportionally smaller than in man. And because he cannot talk, the ape can communicate nothing to us of his conscious experience with which the brain, unlike other organs, is concerned.

When it comes to the lower forms of experimental animals on which we depend in so much of our research, the differences are striking. If the area in the brain of a rat known as the *visual cortex* is destroyed, the rat can still make good use of its eyesight. When jumping about, the little creature judges distance and direction accurately and can distinguish degrees of light. A man injured in this way will be completely blind. Thus while we lean heavily on animals in our scientific studies, we must remember that rats and dogs, monkeys and apes are not human beings and that what is true for them is not necessarily true for us.

Today the secrets of the human brain are being sought in the electrical patterns of its nerve cells, in its biochemical machinery, in its giant protein molecules, in its blood supply, and—because of the analogy between human and "man-made brains"—in the study of electronic computers. But in seeking clues to the brain's deepest mysteries, man is being uniquely human. The clever ape shows skill in solving problems, and even animals with much simpler nervous systems are capable of remembering, learning, and planning. But only man has a brain which insists upon studying itself. This is his human heritage.

While it is true that the ape possesses simple forms of most human mental processes, for all his haunting resemblance to us the ape's intelligence does not exceed that of a four-year-old child. The gap between man and beast remains formidable and irrevocable The ape can be taught to use a knife and fork and to ride a bicycle; he will "ape" our ways. But despite all the patient attempts, no one has yet been able to teach an ape to talk. If you doubt the role of language in making us human, try to produce your next thought without using words to "tell it to yourself."

The use of language is closely linked to our superior ability to think, for words are the symbols we use when we reason and compare. Just as mathematical symbols make it possible for us to solve problems without counting actual objects, words enable us to test the course of an action in our minds without going through the slow and often dangerous process of performing it.

Language not only provides the units of thought, it is also the custodian of knowledge. Unlike humbler animals, whose accumulated experience dies with them, man is able to preserve in spoken and written language all that he has learned, so that even centuries later his descendants receive a tidy inheritance of knowledge. Today the high-school student with an average brain knows more science than the most brilliant individuals who lived four hundred years ago— yet the human brain has not changed.

Throughout his long history man has not only possessed the gift of language but he has also made tools. When the earliest human beings discovered that a piece of flint could be flaked to form a convenient tool for catching and carving supper, man escaped from the blind force of evolution. In the struggle for survival the human being learned to use his brain to control his environment, rather than waiting for the slow process of evolution to adapt him to the stern and often fickle demands of that environment. Today, with the aid of the magnificent tools which are the descendants of those first crude hand axes, man can fly faster and higher than birds without growing wings, he can roam the seas and lakes of his planet without gills, and with his everyday lungs and a special suit he has already ventured forth into the airless world of space.

Language, tools—and what else? Unlike the ape, who is content if his next meal is provided for, man is a creature with a sense of time: He has been somewhere; he is going someplace. He is the only animal who looks forward into the future and dreams of touching the stars. He alone turns around and peers down the ages into the shrouded past. The Book of Genesis, which tells us that in the beginning "the earth was without form, and void; and darkness was upon the face of the deep," expresses this quest for man's roots as much as the reports of a modern geophysical study. In turn, because you are human, you will ask your parents to tell you stories of their childhood, you will explore mankind's near and far history as it is recorded in books, and eventually you will journey backward to a dim, lost time when the earth itself was not yet born. Even there you will be unwilling to rest, for the convenient concepts of the infinite and the eternal in no way satisfy man's insatiable need to know everything. At the same time that man seeks his bearings in time, he looks within and seeks himself. What he has found there we know from his literature, his art, his music, his concepts of right and wrong, and his uniquely human emotions—faith, hope, and love.

And so inevitably we are drawn to the study of the human brain, for it is the physical representation of all that we are and all that we may yet become. As we unravel the deep mysteries of this vast jungle of nerve cells, we begin to appreciate how much of this story still remains to be written. There is a fascinating possibility that in the future man's brain can be put to greater and better use. To understand what our brain means to us, let us start by going back more than seventy-five million years when slow-moving dinosaurs still ruled the land and weird sea monsters swam in ancient, inland seas, to a time when brains were already remarkable, but not yet human.

2

ON THE WAY TO MAN

Throughout most of the Mesozoic era, sometimes called the Age of Reptiles, primitive mammals scurried about, lost in the shadows of the mighty dinosaurs who lumbered through the gloomy swamps and giant softwood forests (see table, Fig. 1). In the beginning of the Cretaceous, the period which marks the last chapter in the reign of the giant reptiles, the earth cooled. Inland seas receded, marshes dried up, and the monster dinosaurs clambered out onto the trembling uplands and began to live on open ground. Great hardwood forests of oak, walnut, beech, and laurel bloomed and soon covered the land. Life for the small, ancestral mammals was perilous, and while the terrible dinosaurs ruled, the little animals hurried about in the deep green shade of the forests or took refuge in the branches of bushes and trees, often venturing forth only at night. They waited, unaware of the kingdom they were soon to inherit, and used their wits and mammalian advantages to survive.

Suddenly, at the end of the Cretaceous, about seventy-five million years ago, in what is one of the great unsolved mysteries of evolution, the terrible dragons vanished from the earth. The humble mammals were at last free to inherit a pleasant, subtropical earth. Who would have dreamed in that time of ravening monsters and walking fortresses that it would be the timid, furtive mammals which would attend the funeral procession of the "terrible lizards" and in time flourish and multiply to produce all the ancestors of the mammals we know today, including man himself?

Eventually it turned out that it was better to be a mammal than a reptile, for although not as extravagant as the gaudy reptiles, the mammals were an improvement in basic animal design. Unlike the cold-blooded reptiles the furry mammals were warm-blooded and possessed an inner thermostat which enabled them to maintain a constant body temperature despite reasonable variations in outside temperature. A reptile faced with chilly weather slows down and becomes lethargic. If it gets colder, the animal either sinks into the oblivion of sleep or it dies. At best this is an awkward way of dealing with the weather. The reptile lays its eggs and, unconcerned, moves on, leaving them to hatch as well as they can, but true mammals bear their young alive, suckle them during infancy, and hover solicitously over their offspring until they are able to fend for themselves. Thus in the intimacy of even the simplest family relationship, the mammalian wits were sharpened. The brain tells the story. It was at this time that the cerebrum—the newer part of the brain, concerned

Fig. 1   TABLE OF GEOLOGIC TIME AND EVOLUTION OF PRINCIPAL FORMS OF ANIMAL LIFE

Era	Period	Epoch	Millions Of Years Ago	Most Common Forms of Life
CENOZOIC "Age of Mammals" 75 million years' duration	Quatenary 1 million years' duration	Recent	0.025	Man
		Pleistocene	1	
				Man-apes
	Tertiary 74 million years' duration	Pliocene	12	
		Miocene	28	Monkeys, apes appear
		Oligocene	39	
		Eocene	58	Mammals
		Paleocene	75	dominate earth
MESOZOIC "Age of Reptiles" 130 million years' duration	Cretaceous 60 million years' duration	Epoch names omitted	135	Primitive mammals increase; dinosaurs become extinct, etc.
	Jurassic 30 million years' duration		165	Dinosaurs dominate; birds, mammals appear
	Triassic 40 million years' duration		205	Dinosaurs appear
PALEOZOIC "Age of Amphibians"	Permian 25 million years' duration	Epoch names omitted	230	Trilobites extinct; amphibians and reptiles continue to develop

Era	Period	Epoch	Millions Of Years Ago	Most Common Forms of Life
300 million years' duration	*Pennsylvanian* 25 million years' duration		255	Reptiles, insects appear
	Mississippian 25 million years' duration		280	
	Devonian 45 million years' duration		325	Fish abundant; amphibians appear
PALEOZOIC	*Silurian* 35 million years' duration		360	Fish develop; first land invertebrates, including scorpions
	Ordovician 65 million years' duration		425	Invertebrates dominate; primitive fish appear, etc.
	Cambrian 80 million years' duration		505	Beginning of fossil record; trilobites and nearly all invertebrate phyla
PRE-CAMBRIAN 1500 years' duration	Period divisions not well established	Epoch names omitted	over 2,000	First forms of life; soft-bodied marine animals; almost no fossils

BASED ON G. G. SIMPSON AND COLBERT

with memory, thinking, and the important business of making decisions—began to enlarge.

Perhaps the gigantic flesh-eating dinosaur Tyrannosaurus Rex could afford a brain which did little more than work the brute's murderous jaws and handle its limited perceptions, for while it survived, Tyrannosaurus terrorized the land and feared no living creature. Stegosaurus, an awkward, humpbacked beast of an earlier period, weighed ten tons, yet its small pointed head carried only two and a half ounces of brain. In fact, Stegosaurus was better equipped aft than fore. Its powerful hind legs and deadly tail were operated by a sacral ganglion, the "hip-brain," which was about twenty times larger than its brain. The mammalian brain was forged in difficult and desperate circumstances, and it is obvious that intelligence and an acute awareness of the surrounding world were necessary if the primitive mammal was to forage for its food and at the same time avoid becoming a dinosaur's dinner.

On the Ground—Smell-Brains

One of these archaic mammals—a tiny insect-eater about the size of a mouse—belonged to the order of *insectivores*, which include hedgehogs, moles, and shrews (see Fig. 2). The little creature had a long snout and five digits on each foot, which it used for digging, climbing, and grasping. It is related to the modern tree shrew, which survives today in the Indonesian forests. Quick, hungry, but daring to hunt

Fig. 2 *Examples of nonhuman primates. The gorilla is supporting (from left to right): tree shrew, lemur, tarsier, and monkey (not drawn to scale).*

only at night, the little insectivore scampering among the low bushes and dank leaves of the dark forest floor fathered the order of *primates*, which include—among living species—tree shrews, lemurs, tarsiers, monkeys, apes, and man. It appears a modest beginning, but in about seventy-five million years the road from an ancient insectivore led up into the trees and down again to man.

The weak eyes of the shrewlike insectivore were set on either side of its head, and it depended on its keen sense of smell to escape its enemies and to hunt the insects and find the berries on which it thrived. The little animal had a respectable mammalian brain, but for all that it was still what is called a "smell-brain." Since the insectivore lived or died by its sense of smell, the area in the brain devoted to smell dominated. By its nose and by its brain, the insectivore was tied to the smell of creeping mold and rotting logs which carpeted the forest aisles.

While ancestral birds grew wings to escape their enemies and other mammals developed horns, hoofs, or fangs, a shrewlike animal climbed into the trees for safety, and there in the high branches, at the dawn of Tertiary time, the die was cast in the direction of man.

Up into the Trees—Eye-Brains

In the *Origin of Species*, in which he presented his great theory of evolution by natural selection, Charles Darwin observed that in the struggle for existence those animals and plants survived which were best equipped to meet the challenge of their surroundings. Upon reproducing they often transmitted their favorable endowment to their offspring. One of the most important agents of evolution is an alteration in the genetic machinery of the cell known as a *mutation*.

The hereditary traits of plants and animals are carried in tiny units called *genes*, which are distributed along the much larger *chromosomes* present in the nucleus of the living cell. Sometimes a gene is accidentally altered, and this change, or mutation, when inherited by the offspring, may appear as a new characteristic. Most mutations are harmful. In a changing environment, however, the new characteristic may be useful and will be retained. In this way succeeding generations are slowly altered by the interplay of genetic accident and a relentless, ever-changing environment which tolerates only those specimens that adapt to its conditions.

Life in the tree tops remodeled the primate body, changed his family life, developed his senses, and put a premium on good eyesight. The sunlit, sociable world of the forest roof broadens an animal's horizons, but tree life has rather practical requirements if the creature which spends its time swinging or jumping from bough to bough is to be a success. Those animals that lose their balance or misjudge the distance between branches often pay with their lives, while the animals with superior equipment for trapeze life survive to produce others endowed like themselves.

Arm walking, or "brachiating" as it is called, requires grasping (prehensile) hands which can hold a limb securely, as well as flexible forearms and swiveling shoulder joints. A man can swing his arm through the air to throw a ball, a monkey can hunt for his fleas, but a horse's legs, although designed for speed, can do little else but remain under him. The nimble, flexible hand, with a thumb opposing the palm, found other uses in the tree-top world. It is much safer to crouch securely on a branch and extend a single arm for a tasty bird's egg than to risk snout and body in the direction of dinner. Nor is a branch a good table; it is more practical for the animal to hold the food safely in its hands and peel fruit or shell a nut with agile, separate fingers.

Anyone who has climbed a tree appreciates the importance of good balance to the jungle acrobat. To meet this demand the part of the brain controlling sensations coming from the muscles and from the balance mechanism in the inner ear began to enlarge. Sharp *stereoscopic vision*, which gives an accurate sense of position and depth, is also essential if an animal as heavy as an ape or monkey is to make its way safely from branch to branch. Here in the dry, sunlit world of the forest roof, the ancient sense of smell, so useful to animals that grub in the moist earth, lost much of its value, and the task of bringing the outer world into the animal's brain was taken over chiefly by vision. This change is illustrated first by the development of the brains and bodies of the furry lemurs and tiny tarsiers that descended from the early shrewlike insectivore and later by the anatomical development of the monkeys and apes that appeared in the forest about forty to fifty million years ago.

The lemur, still found in the primeval forests of Africa and Asia, made some of the earliest experiments in developing the human design (see Fig. 2). The lemur is a nocturnal animal with a foxlike snout and huge eyes, which are situated somewhat forward in its head. He has a spidery, five-fingered hand that looks more human than even the monkey or ape hand, in which the thumb is often stunted. The lemur took a timid, tentative step in the human direction but pursued this interesting course no further. He had then, and in his modern form still has, a smell-brain.

At about this time there lived in the trees a funny, gnomelike animal known as a *tarsier* (see Fig. 2). The large family of ancient tarsiers has long since disappeared from the earth, and only one form, a living ghost, survives today almost unchanged in the Indonesian jungles and in the Philippines. He is the affectionate, woolly *Spectral Tarsier*, which carries within its pert head the early secrets of the human brain. Unlike the lemur, the tarsier possesses a primitive form of the more sophisticated eye-brain, in which the visual areas are enlarged, while the olfactory (smell) regions are diminished. The living tarsier is no bigger than a squirrel, has prehensile hands, a long tufted tail, and enormous, gleaming eyes—round as saucer plates—which have won it the name "Spectral." Its eyes are set in the front of its head and, significantly, the muzzle has shrunk, giving the tarsier the suggestion of a face.

Animals such as the dog, whose eyes, separated by a muzzle, are placed on either side of its head, see entirely different visual fields with each eye. The tarsier's vision, known as *parallel vision*, is a step forward but is an imperfect form of stereoscopic, or depth, vision. In order to obtain a sense of depth, the tarsier must focus each eye separately and then rotate its head. The *convergent vision* of monkeys, apes, and man, who have true stereoscopic vision, makes it possible for them to focus automatically and sharply with both eyes at the same time. Since there is no obstructing muzzle, the visual field of each eye overlaps, and the object in focus then appears either nearer or farther than the other objects around it. To discover the rich, three-dimensional world in which most of us live, cover one eye and stand at an arm's length from a table. Then try to strike the edge of the table with your index finger. You will misjudge the distance on the first attempt. Now try it with both eyes open. Once again cover one eye and look around the room. Although shadows and perspective give clues to depth, it is suddenly and uneasily a much flatter, less precise world.

As eyes and hands explored the colorful, gay world of the subtropical forests, the brain began to expand. Color vision, known to fish, insects, and birds, reappeared in monkeys. The colors of exotic fruit, the patterns of leaves, and the texture of gnarled tree bark became the "food" for a new, hungry brain which responded not only by increasing the area allotted to its lively senses but by developing the large storage areas of memory. Many of the automatic, instinctive circuits disappeared, and now, slowly, encouraged by its lively senses, the brain began to awaken from its ancient, mindless sleep.

It is interesting that much that is human in our own brain originated in the family life of the early primates. Since the primate infant hung on to its mother while she climbed and swung through the branches, large litters became impractical and the primate settled down to bearing and raising one offspring at a time. To the mother of a single baby, her only child becomes particularly precious; at the same time she can lavish more care and attention on her offspring. The monkey washing her baby, scolding it when it disobeys, or reading the expression on its funny, mobile face needs an intelligent and flexible brain. Here is life beyond the archaic patterns of the sleepwalking creatures whose destinies from birth to death are largely determined by inborn circuits of reflex and instinct. The brain which regulates this type of intimate family life may not be prepared to consider the distant future, but it must be capable of remembering. It must be aware of what is going on in its own limited world, and it must be able to respond intelligently. What was once never-known becomes known and is remembered, and now the patterns of decision trace their mysterious routes over the nerve pathways which have begun to fill the dark recesses of the growing brain.

And Down Again

At what point and for what reason our tree-dwelling primate ancestor left the trees and came down to the ground we are not certain. One theory is that the trees disappeared. More likely our ancestor simply became too heavy for tree life. Before he abandoned the trees completely and set out to roam the earth, there undoubtedly was a transition stage during which large, apelike animals continued their arboreal life, making short excursions to the ground. Fortunately in his ground expeditions this creature did not return to his predecessor's four-legged gait. At the same time he brought with him the improvements in body and brain won during his long life as a trapeze artist.

The fossil record from which we must read the story of millions of years of evolution is still sketchy, and repeatedly we shall find not one, but many "missing links." By the early Miocene, some twenty million years ago, there lived in Africa and Asia a variety of apelike animals all of which are now extinct. One of these creatures, named *Proconsul*, resembled the modern chimpanzee, although less specialized in ape-like characteristics. Proconsul may have been the common ancestor of both the modern anthropoid (manlike) apes seen in our zoos and of man (see ape, Fig. 2). Another relatively unspecialized fossil ape,

Dryopithecus (tree ape), lived somewhat later in the Miocene and is considered by many primatologists to be the forerunner of modern apes and man. It has also been suggested that the line which led to man branched off even earlier, about thirty to forty million years ago during Oligocene times. *Parapithecus*, one of the earliest apelike fossils, dates from this epoch. Whether Parapithecus was an early monkey or an early ape remains a matter of debate. Unfortunately this small, apelike primate is represented by nothing more than a fragment of a jaw bone, and until more complete evidence is found we can only contemplate the reconstructions of our fossil relatives and wonder which of these ancient creatures, if any, was man's direct ancestor. One thing is certain: The large, intelligent apes alive today are possibly our cousins, but certainly not our ancestors. As the most intelligent of the nonhuman primates they are, however, interesting and intriguing, for they suggest an earlier stage in our long journey. And by their curious, incomplete resemblance to us they emphasize the vast gulf which separates man from even the most manlike of the beasts.

The living anthropoid apes include the acrobatic gibbon, the orangutan, the chimpanzee, and the gorilla. In size, in brain structure, and in their social and family behavior the chimpanzee and gorilla are most like us. The lively, sociable chimpanzee is considered by many to be the closer to man in intelligence. But

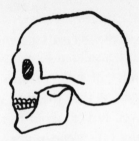

HOMO SAPIENS
Brain capacity: 1400 cc. (av.)

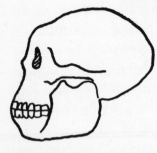

PITHECANTHROPUS ERECTUS
Brain capacity: 900 cc.

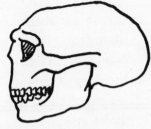

NEANDERTHAL MAN
Brain capacity: 1450 to 1625 cc.

AUSTRALOPITHECUS
Brain capacity: 650 cc.

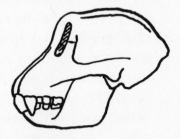

CHIMPANZEE
Brain capacity: 400 cc.

Fig. 3   *Evolution of man's skull*

the structure of the gorilla's nervous system is more like ours, and his physical resemblance to man is greater. It is only fair to add that because of his great size, his shy and often brutish temperament, the adult gorilla is difficult to study.

The chimpanzee has a cranial capacity of about 400 cc. (see Fig. 3) . The much heavier gorilla has a brain case of about 550 cc. On the ground both apes prefer a semierect position, supporting some of their weight on the knuckles of their hands. The gorilla and the chimpanzee can stand fully erect if they choose, but examination of an ape's skull reveals the reason why this feat is not so simple. The ape's spine joins the skull toward the rear, whereas the human spine joins at the center of the skull so that the skull is comfortably balanced on top of the spine. The huge gorilla requires massive neck muscles to keep his great jaws and muzzle from falling forward. In fact the apparent height of the gorilla skull is deceptive, for part of the skull, the high sagittal crest, which runs from front to back along the vault, is used to support the powerful muscles which move the lower jaw. The actual brain space is surprisingly small. This fact is significant, for if brain size is to increase, the skull must devote itself to housing the brain rather than supporting heavy jaw bones, powerful muscles, and a snout.

At some unknown point, perhaps ten to twelve million years ago in the Pliocene, our apelike ancestor left the protection of the forest and stepped out onto the broad, open plains (see table, Fig. 1). If we dare to telescope the stately pace of evolution, we might imagine that one such creature held in his hand a stone he had picked up to examine. Toward him, through the tall grass, crept a wildcat stalking its prey. For a moment the creature holding the stone hesitated, thinking desperately of the trees at the edge of the forest. And then in some way realizing that he had come too far and that it was too late, he took aim and hurled the stone. Surprised, the cat turned and fled through the rippling grass. It is true that apes use sticks and stones as primitive tools, but as long as an ape needs its hands for climbing, tools remain an amusement, a luxury, and are not to be depended on seriously. For this creature, no longer ape but not yet man, it was different. Having eyes which could focus properly, a brain which understood the significance of the situation, and a flexible limb now emancipated from locomotor duties, our progenitor discovered the considerable advantage of using tools to help manipulate his destiny.

The transition from trees to ground did not come suddenly, but in the end our ancestor exchanged the safety of the trees for the freedom of the ground. This was the first step in a restless journey which would eventually take him the length and breadth of his planet, to its mountain peaks and ocean valleys, until one day he would finally set out on the trail of other worlds. Gradually his pelvis would broaden, his legs would grow longer and straighter and terminate in a true foot, and his skull would balance comfortably on top of his upright spine. Just before the dawn of man our unknown ancestor walked erect and his dexterous hands, conveniently placed within view of his sharp stereoscopic eyes, were at last fully free to begin man's work. This was the fateful combination. Yet one thing was lacking—a suitable brain.

Fig. 4 *Portrait of Australopithecus*

Body in Search of a Brain

For many years scholars have debated whether man first acquired his human body and then his brain or whether an expanding brain inspired a body which could make use of its new intelligence. Then in 1925 the fossil skull of *Australopithecus africanus* (southern ape of Africa) was found, and with the subsequent discovery of other Australopithecine remains, the question was answered (see Fig. 4) . Half a million to a million years ago and perhaps earlier, man-apes, creatures with human bodies and apelike heads, walked the earth upright, retreated to caves for protection and shelter, and perhaps—here evidence is thin—knew how to make very primitive tools. The bones of the legs and pelvis and the opening in the base of the skull, which is set further forward than in the ape, indicate that the Australopithecines walked upright and had a true foot with which to run. Although the teeth were more human than apelike, the Australopithecine skull was basically that of an ape. Its vault was low, some forms even had the gorilla's sagittal crest, and its hollow of about 650 cc. housed a brain somewhat larger than a gorilla's (see Fig. 3) .

Today scientists feel that these pre-men were probably too specialized in an apelike direction to have been our direct ancestors. Furthermore, the more recent fossils come from a period half a million years ago when there were already true human beings inhabiting the earth. These subhuman creatures could not have been the ancestors of men living at the same time. Nevertheless Australopithecus fascinates us because he is a link with that inconceivable twilight world, halfway between man and beast. He proves that first man walked erect and only then did he conjure the spirits of fire and water and listen to his own thoughts speaking to him.

With the appearance of the lemur the brain slowly began to grow larger. Animals that lacked swift legs, great strength, horns, and fangs—those that were gradually losing their built-in protective instincts—had to use their wits if they were to avoid the road which leads to extinction. But for millions of years the rate of brain expansion had been gradual and slow. Suddenly the brain seems to have embarked on an amazing spurt of growth in what is, geologically speaking, but a breath of time. The speed with which a half-wild brain became a human brain remains one of the deep mysteries of evolution. Fossil evidence is still meager and dating techniques are not always reliable. In the end we may discover that we have paced man's evolution incorrectly, but at present it appears that man got his brain in a hurry.

We belong to the species *Homo sapiens* (homo = man; sapiens = wise), the only species of man which has survived. The exact date of the appearance of Homo sapiens is still being debated. Some authorities feel he may be as old as 200,000 years. Certainly the handsome Cro-Magnons, who lived 25,000 years ago in southern Europe, were true members of our species. Cro-Magnon man was six feet tall, had a larger brain case than ours (up to 1650 cc.), and was a cave artist of extraordinary skill. But we know neither from where he came nor among what people he originated.

By "man," however, we mean more than Homo

sapiens. Before they became extinct there were other members of the genus Homo. Short, stocky *Homo neanderthalensis* (Neanderthal man), who lived 150,000 to 50,000 years ago in late Pleistocene times and endured the last of the Ice Ages, is one example. Despite his sloping forehead and heavy jaws, Neanderthal man had a brain which in some cases was larger than our own (1450 to 1625 cc.). Although he is the favorite subject for cave-man humor, in his behavior Neanderthal man seems to have been entirely human. He made scraping and piercing tools, clothed himself in animal skins, used fire, and buried his dead. Whatever his motives may have been, it is certain from this evidence that he knew the meaning of death and that dreams, symbols, and superstitions had already wound their complex pathways among the cells of his brain.

Much earlier, perhaps half a million years ago, there lived more primitive men whose brains had not yet reached the range of modern man. One such ancient man, *Pithecanthropus erectus* (Java man), had a cranial capacity of about 900 cc. (see Fig. 3). The brain of *Pithecanthropus pekinensis* (Peking man), who lived somewhat later, was about 1100 cc. in volume and closer to that of modern man, whose average cranial capacity is 1400 cc. Peking man lived in caves, cooked his meat, and made simple tools. There is some evidence that he was a cannibal and that he ate the brains of his victims. Eating brains or drinking an enemy's blood from a skull goblet may have been an attempt to acquire some of the wisdom and power of the dead. It is not a pretty idea, but it does hint that Peking man was aware of the spirit of man and that his brain already contained the dimensions of imagination, ritual, and superstition.

The evolutionary road which leads to us has not been a straight and simple path. Here and there on this journey of more than a million years a fossil is found—perhaps a broken skull and a long leg bone or a jaw with one or two ancient teeth. For a moment there is a break in the swirling mists and we glimpse what we once were—or what we never were. There have been many turnings, many blind alleys, but only one road led to us. Which one? We still do not know. Only recently the fossil skull of an ancient primitive man related to the Australopithecines and called *Zinjanthropus boisei* was discovered in Tanganyika. It appears that over a million years ago Zinjanthropus walked erect in East Africa and although small-brained, made primitive pebble tools. Since tool making is usually considered the entrance requirement for human status, this—if it is true—would add at least a half million years to the previously accepted span of human evolution.

The Human Formula

While nameless fossils still sleep at buried crossroads, we must turn to another question: What did

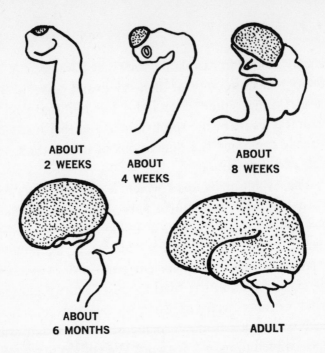

ABOUT 2 WEEKS

ABOUT 4 WEEKS

ABOUT 8 WEEKS

ABOUT 6 MONTHS

ADULT

Fig. 5 *Development of the human brain showing growth of cerebrum (dotted areas)* BASED ON HERRICK

the brain need to become human? First it had to grow larger, for a large brain provides more working space (see Fig. 5). However it is not the smell areas of the brain nor any of the ancient regions controlling vital life functions which are enlarged, but rather the frontal lobes of the cerebrum, particularly the part hidden behind our high foreheads. This is the area of the brain which considers, compares, plans, and even worries. Here, too, may be located certain of the speech centers which shape the words that carry our thoughts. Although the ape can solve problems intelligently, his brain tethers him loosely to the present, and his memory is limited to events in his own life. He knows no *other* ape's life. It is the frontal region of the brain—the part that pushes the forehead out to a vertical position —which contains the routes into the far past, the units of mind needed to imagine the future and, most of all, to be aware of the life of another creature.

In addition to its size the human brain has acquired an unusual growth schedule. The special priority given to the brain is apparent very early in the development of the human embryo. As the head of the baby forms, the brain area develops first, and the skull bones and face must manage with what space is left. At birth the human infant is preposterously large-brained (330 cc.), with an unfinished, almost jawless face and a body which will take years to complete its growth. Since the mother's pelvis places a limit on the size of the human skull at birth, the brain is born incomplete and must accomplish most of its growth after birth.

The timetable governing the pace of human brain growth is unique and quickly takes our brain far beyond the shrewd animal brain of even the most intelligent ape. In the first year of life the brain grows very rapidly, and when we are about three years old it reaches two-thirds of its full size. After this it continues to grow slowly, and the weaving of its invisible mental pathways continues throughout most of adult life.

The gorilla brain is more complete at birth, and for this greater degree of prepackaging, the gorilla pays a price. He will walk at six months, be independent in about a year, and mature in about six to eight years, but before the ape has a chance to learn anything his brain has accomplished more than half of its growth. While the human being, even as an adult, retains his childlike face, his high skull, and small jaws, the mature ape loses his former haunting resemblance to the human child and develops the powerful jaws, thick skull, and massive muscles of the beast. Intelligence often diminishes in the adult ape. Frequently morose, he becomes difficult to teach and may forget what man has already taught him. This is understandable since apes were intended to live a jungle life and not to imitate human beings in zoos and on television programs.

A brain born unfinished and a prolonged childhood —this, then, is the human secret. Only in the human family do children of different ages still live in the home of their parents. Throughout his lengthened infancy and the long, dependent years of childhood, the human being has a young, growing brain hungry for knowledge and eager for exercise. More than in any other animal, it is very much a personal brain, un-committed to preset patterns of behavior, richly en-dowed with nerve cells, sensitive, curious, waiting to be inscribed with its own story. Unlike that of the gifted ape, the human being's mental ability continues to increase. Far from wilting, the intelligent, experi-enced, well-cultivated human brain bears the finest fruit of human endeavor—wisdom. For Homo sapiens means the *wise* man, not merely the intelligent man, and although we may complain that too often man does not seem to be so wise, wisdom is the standard against which his brain must finally be measured.

Is this the end of the story? Is the brain of Homo sapiens the best there will ever be? We have no reason to believe this is so. Yet before we peer out to where the winds of the future blow and uneasy atoms whirl, we must first make certain that man makes the best possible use of the brain he already has, for man's brain has given him the awesome power to modify his environment without altering his own body. Seventy-five million years after his tiny, frightened ancestor scurried up into the trees, man holds within his soft, sensitive, deeply convoluted brain the destiny of all the living creatures which share this planet with him —including his fellow men.

3

NERVE CELLS
AND TRAFFIC PATTERNS

Origins

The human nervous system consists of the brain, the spinal cord, and the vast network of nerves which run near and far to every part of the body. But long before the first nerve cell developed, the possibility of nerve conduction was contained within the protoplasm of the smallest unit of life, the cell. Every living cell, whether plant or animal, has the ability to respond to a change in its environment known as a *stimulus*. This characteristic, called *irritability*, is one of the basic requirements for life. Because its protoplasm is irritable, the complex plant, which has no nerve cells, nevertheless turns its leaves toward the sunlight; and a one-celled animal such as the amoeba moves in the direction of food or out of harm's way.

Compared with animal life, however, plant life is relatively undramatic. Most plants are ingenious chemical laboratories producing their own food from the water, air, and sunlight around them. Animals, even those no larger than a single microscopic cell, are hunters, not chemists, and must find their food ready-made in the form of plants and other animals. In all but the very lowest animal forms this involves some degree of movement. In searching for food, it is necessary to have some system which assures that the organism goes in the right direction at the right time. It is also highly desirable to avoid becoming someone else's food. Here, in the animal's need for coordination and direction, lies the reason for the origin of the nervous system.

The one-celled amoeba has always done well enough without a nervous system. As cells came together, to form more complex animals, the single cell, jack-of-all-trades, was no longer practical. Instead cells began to specialize: Some which could contract became muscles, others became rigid to form scaffolding, secreting cells became glands. Still others, in which the protoplasm had spun out into long, thin tentacles capable of receiving and conducting electrical charges, became nerve cells.

The forerunner of a true nervous system is found in the *coelenterates*, which include marine animals such as the jellyfish and the sea anemone. The nerve cells of the jellyfish are joined in a continuous nerve net which connects all parts of the animal. However the primitive nerve net indiscriminately conducts impulses in all directions at the same time. It is a communication system which still lacks "central control," and as a result the sea anemone will retract the region around its mouth whether you stimulate the mouth itself, the body of the animal, or its tentacles.

This type of response works well enough for the drifting jellyfish or the slow-moving anemone, but it would hardly do for the spiny-skinned *echinoderms*— animals such as the starfish and sea urchin. Should each of the five rays of the starfish insist upon crawling in a different direction in search of food, the poor starfish would go nowhere and would soon starve to death. To prevent such a biological tragedy, the starfish is provided with a primitive form of central control. The animal has a central ring of nerve cells with a nerve running out to each ray. The central ring coordinates the arms of the starfish so that the one pointing in the direction of food becomes the leader and the remaining four follow until the mission is accomplished. This evolutionary advance, however, does not mean that the starfish evolved directly from the jellyfish any more than we did from the chimpanzee. The family tree in Fig. 6 explains some of the relationships among the *invertebrates*, those small animals without backbones who comprise about 95 per cent of all the species of the animal kingdom.

The radial form of the echinoderms was not destined to be the design of the *vertebrates*, those creatures with backbones who evolved from an unknown invertebrate and eventually crawled out of the waters and inherited the earth (see detailed classification, pages 279–281). Even as the starfish inched its way along the ocean floor, an ambitious primitive flatworm had

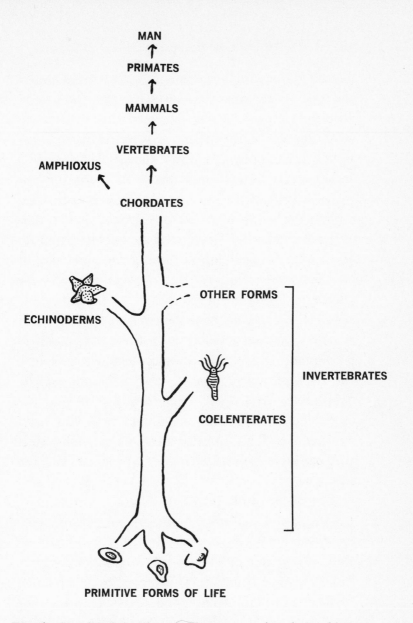

Fig. 6 *Simplified family tree showing man's relationship to his chordate and invertebrate ancestors*

already begun early experiments with a prototype of the kind of nervous system which, some two billion years later, was to become our own.

As animals began to move actively through the waters, it was only natural that they should develop a front part, a "head." Since the "head" was the first to reach the new environment, it discovered that environment before body or tail arrived. The worms evolved a system of "feedback" in which the forward part of the animal gathers information and relays it to lower centers which use this information to produce appropriate behavior in the animal. At the same time the outlying stations keep the front end informed of what has occurred so that future action can be modified accordingly. In the more advanced segmented worms, the nervous system consists of a series of *ganglia* (clusters of nerve cells) arranged along the long axis of the body. Additional nerves run from this main nerve cord to the various segments of the body, while the head end is dominated by a slightly larger ganglion, the brain.

Thus many invertebrates, such as the worms and insects, utilized the feedback principle, but unfortunately their nervous system developed so that it surrounded the digestive system or ran along the front of the body below the digestive tract. This proved to be a mistake because the brain soon found itself competing for space with the animal's esophagus, and in the crisis which developed the choice between starvation or an intellectual future was inevitably resolved in favor of survival.

Another design was tried by the slender, fishlike lancet known as *Amphioxus*, a "lower" chordate and primitive relative of the vertebrates (see Fig. 7). This proved more practical. In Amphioxus the digestive clutter was avoided because its nerve cord, by now a single, hollow tube like our own spinal cord, was situated *above* the digestive system. Immediately

NERVE CORD   **TAIL**

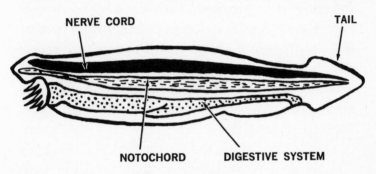

NOTOCHORD   **DIGESTIVE SYSTEM**

Fig. 7 *Amphioxus*

below the nerve cord there was also a flexible, unsegmented rod known as the *notochord*, which served as a support for the muscles the animal would need if it planned to do any serious swimming. In the higher vertebrates the primitive notochord is replaced by a true segmented vertebral column, the spine, which surrounds and protects the spinal cord.

And so the brain was born in the slight swelling at

the forward end of animals that had need of moving about in the warm, primeval seas. This became the successful pattern: a long, hollow tube running down the back of the animal, from which nerves are distributed to the various segments of the body—and a master ganglion. And this still remains the pattern in the thinking, two-legged animal who counts an unknown, fishlike creature somewhere near the blurred base of his family tree.

The development of any animal while it is still an embryo tells in telescoped form the story of its forefathers' evolution. This does not mean that we become fish and frogs in the nine months before we become man, but the embryo does retravel many of the routes which have proved successful for the production of a human being—including some which no longer seem important.

To form its nervous system, the human embryo follows the example of Amphioxus and actually uses the skin of its back. First there is a thickening in the skin down the midline of the back, and by the time the embryo is three weeks old, this strip sinks into a groove. Quickly the margins of the groove rise, and one week later they close to form the primitive neural tube, now buried beneath the surface of the skin. Already the basic parts of the brain are being sketched in, and nerves and ganglia have begun to form. In time, all that will be left of the original hollow tube will be the small central canal of the spinal cord and four cavities, or *ventricles*, within the brain itself.

It is with awe that we watch this early shifting, pleating, and folding in an embryo still no bigger than a pea. If the neural tube does not close properly or should a few cells fail to go to their appointed destinations, the embryo is immediately doomed either to death or to serious malformation. The wonder is that this happens so rarely.

Information and Control

What does a nervous system mean to a creature as complex as a human being? And to what extent is our nervous system true to the heritage of its primitive forerunner, which evolved so that an animal might move?

The human body consists of trillions of cells arranged in various organs and systems. Some of these cells support the body, others form its covering, some fight disease, some become blood, others pump that blood, and all of these cells are the offspring of one cell to which is entrusted the secret of life. The organs and systems of the body are immensely talented but specialized units. Yet without the nervous system to organize and command their resources, many would remain idle, while some would use their innate abilities to no avail, perhaps even to destroy each other. Deprived of the central control provided by the brain and its communication system of nerves, right hand would fight left hand, lungs would collapse, and food traffic would snarl hopelessly in the digestive tract. Without the brain the electrical impulses coming from the print on this page would fall upon the light-sensitive cells in the eye and there they would die, for it is the brain which translates nerve impulses; it is the brain which sees. The disaster list is endless, for without the nervous system there can be nothing but chaos.

Although you may be tempted to think of the master organ of the nervous system, the brain, primarily as the place which produces our thoughts and launches our ideas, these higher functions are late-comers. Actually the elaborate mental life of the human brain is very much in the original tradition of all nervous systems, for the primary function of the nervous system, from jellyfish to man, is to enable the organism to *respond appropriately* to its inner and outer environment. This remains its role, whether it directs you to pull back a hand from a hot stove, causes you to blush, or enables you to plan a budget. To look at it another way, the nervous system is responsible for the way we act; it determines and produces our behavior.

As the integrating mechanism of the body, the human nervous system has many duties:

1. It provides the communication routes (nerves)

which ultimately link the sense, or receptor, organs, such as those found in the skin, eyes, and ears, with motor, or effector, organs (muscles and glands).

2. It adjusts behavior to the quality and quantity of a stimulus so that if you prick your finger with a needle, you do not respond as if you had cut it with a knife. If you have simply been clumsy with a sewing needle, you quickly withdraw the injured finger. If your finger is being pricked for a blood test, you brace your arm and hold your finger steady. It is not enough for the body to respond to a stimulus; the response must be appropriate.

3. It coordinates the activities of every part of the body so that the vast army of highly specialized cells assembled in the shape of a human being functions harmoniously.

4. It stores our memories, holds the patterns of habit, and permits us to learn.

5. Finally, it records our dreams and composes our thoughts.

Since it is the nervous system and its senses which make us aware of our environment, it is this same system which selects the specific world in which each of us—you and I, ape, insect, frog and fish—lives. The bat, scarcely able to see, dwells in a world in which rafters, trees, and food sing out to it in the shrill language of supersonic vibrations. The higher the evolutionary level of an animal, the richer is the world its

senses and nervous system construct for it. Despite
what appear to us as limitations, we must remember
that the bat's nervous equipment is perfectly suited to
the bat.

What, we may ask ourselves, is it like to be a dog?
We cannot be certain, but the dog probably lives in a
world in which the present is eternal, where tomorrow
does not exist, and where the past consists of useful
memories culled from one dog's personal experience.
It is a two-dimensional world in which the stage is set
in shades of black and white, quickly receding into a
shadowy blur. It is a world where, instead of green
grass and brown soil, the ground bears rich tales of
other dogs recently gone by, of buried bones and underground moles. The wind, little more than movements of air to us, is, for the dog, alive with the scents
of friend and foe. Above all, if the dog is a pet, his
single, unwavering loyalty to his master floods his
senses, claims many of his instincts, and to a great
extent, dominates whatever must be the mental and
emotional life of a dog.

Even among human beings the physical world is not
necessarily interpreted in the same way. Five people
may give five different reports of the same automobile
accident, and despite our color vision, you and I do
not see quite the same thing in the brilliant hues of the
setting sun. For centuries philosophers have struggled
with the problem of finding the true nature of the
world—that is, the world apart from the special abili-

ties and the bias of our individual nervous systems. Leaving philosophy aside, we shall return to the physiological significance of this theme in Chapter 13, for it has profound implications for all of us.

The Charged Cell

The basic unit of the nervous system is the electrically charged nerve cell called a *neuron.* Neurons which carry incoming impulses to the spinal cord and brain are called *sensory* (afferent) neurons; those which carry instructions back to muscles and glands are called *motor* (efferent) neurons. *Connecting,* or *intermediate,* neurons are the nerve cells which link sensory and motor nerves.

Neurons do not see, nor do they hear or think. They are living dynamos and have the single duty of conducting messages in the form of electrical impulses. When using the term "message," however, we must understand that the electrical impulse carried by the nerve fiber is not a true message. It does not say, even in code or symbolic form, "red" or "blue," "smooth" or "round," "stop" or "go." Impulses traveling along nerve pathways are standard stock, differing only in speed and intensity, and nerve fibers are loyal, unquestioning servants: They do as they are told. The meaning of the message is not determined by the sender, as is true in a telephone communication, but by the region of the brain into which the impulse finally discharges. The reply depends upon the particular

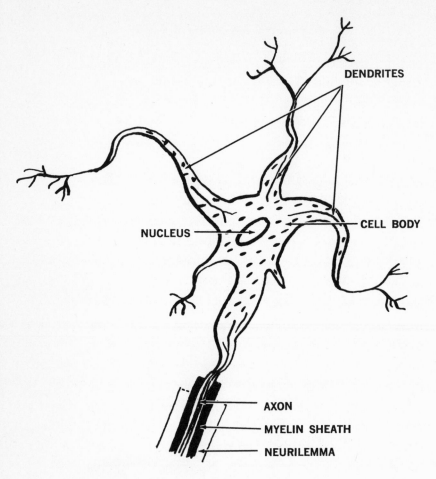

DENDRITES

CELL BODY

NUCLEUS

AXON

MYELIN SHEATH

NEURILEMMA

Fig. 8 *Neuron*

muscle or gland which serves as the terminal for the
motor nerve path. What is more, when unknowingly
you dial a wrong telephone number, you will deliver
the message originally intended. But should the nervous system reach a "wrong number," the message
would be quite different. If, for example, the nerve

endings in the eye were connected to the auditory center in the brain and were the nerve endings in the ear to terminate in the visual center, lightning would be a noise and thunder a vision.

Some neurons are round, some are oval, some pyramidal, but all nerve cells, whether those of a frog, mouse, or man, are easily distinguished by their extensions: the long, trunklike *axon* and the delicate, branching *dendrites* which equip the neuron for its task of receiving and conducting impulses (see Fig. 8). The cell body in the largest human nerve cell is only two thousandths of an inch in diameter, but it may have fibers ranging from a fraction of an inch to two or three feet in length. What we call a nerve, what the surgeon grasps with his forceps, is actually a large bundle of nerve fibers. The eye alone has a million fibers in the optic nerve—its private highway to the brain.

Under the microscope dendrites look like the branches of a tree, dividing again and again into tiny, interlacing twigs. By means of its dendrites a single cell can reach out to neighboring nerve cells, and in this way it not only transmits the impulse entrusted to it but makes the multiple connections needed to produce the complicated responses of the body. Although there may be many dendritic fibers, or processes, there is only one axon. Some axons are covered with a fatty membrane (*myelin sheath*) which gives the fibers a whitish appearance, while others are unmyelinated and, like nerve cell bodies, appear gray in color. As far as we

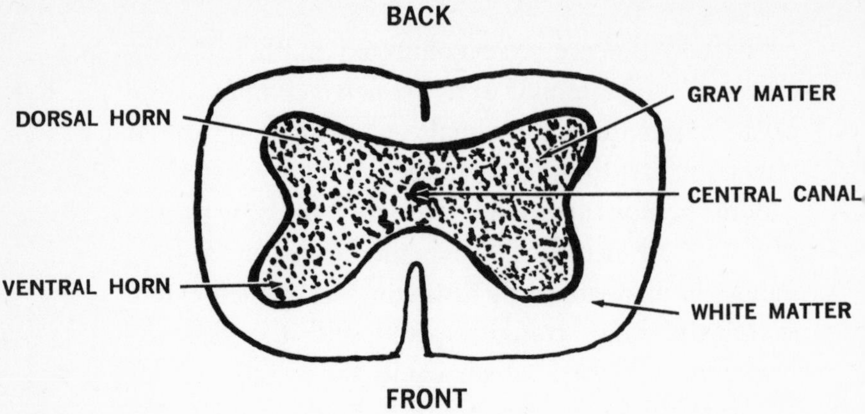

BACK

DORSAL HORN

GRAY MATTER

CENTRAL CANAL

VENTRAL HORN

WHITE MATTER

FRONT

Fig. 9 *Cross section of spinal cord showing gray and white matter*

know, the myelin sheath acts as insulation for the nerve fibers and speeds the rate of conduction. Finally, peripheral nerves, those nerves outside of the brain and spinal cord, are enclosed in a membrane known as the *neurilemma*.

These gray and white color distinctions are very helpful to a study of the nervous system. If you slice across any section of the spinal cord, you will find a rough H-shape, or butterfly pattern, of gray matter in the center. This gray matter contains nerve cell bodies and unmyelinated nerve fibers (see Fig. 9). The outside portion of the spinal cord is white and consists of bundles of nerve fibers, mostly myelinated, running up and down the cord. As the spinal cord reaches the skull and expands to become the brain, the distribution of gray and white matter gradually reverses so that in the cerebrum and the cerebellum, which form the bulk of the human brain, most of the gray matter is on the outside in a thin crust called the *cortex*, while the white matter makes up the core of the brain.

Compared to its far-reaching tendrils, the tiny cell body seems unimpressive, yet it is the heart, the very life, of the nerve cell. If it is destroyed, it is never replaced. If you sever a nerve fiber, the part sectioned from the parent cell slowly degenerates and dies. Nerve fibers in the brain and spinal cord can never be repaired, but those fibers outside the spinal cord have the power of regeneration as long as they have not been separated from their cell body. Slowly the stump of the injured nerve fiber makes its way through the neurilemma, which is all that remains of the lost route, until weeks or perhaps months later it regains contact with the receptor organ or muscle it originally served.

The Cell Fires

Nerve cells operate on what is called the "all or none" principle. Like an ordinary light bulb, a nerve cell is either on or off. Like a gun, it either fires or it does not. If you stimulate the fiber of a nerve cell experimentally with an electric current, once triggered, the strength of the impulse is always the same. The only way to increase or decrease the intensity of the impulse in an individual nerve fiber is to alter the time pattern between stimuli. The largest nerve fibers conduct impulses at the rate of more than three hundred feet per second, or over two hundred miles an hour, so that in the body communication can be almost instantaneous.

When a nerve (a large bundle of nerve fibers) is stimulated, a minute amount of electric current travels down the length of its fibers very much as a spark runs along a fuse. But unlike the fuse, which is destroyed by the spark, a nerve needs only a very brief rest, known as the *refractory period*, and it is ready to go back to work. The impulse travels along the nerve by means of an automatic relay mechanism. Each successive point in the nerve fiber boosts the impulse it has received to full strength and then disturbs the next point. In this manner the impulse is transmitted from point to point, down the line, somewhat in the way a row of bowling pins topple each other. For this reason impulses traveling long distances do not lose strength or clarity before arriving at their final destination. If you step on a sharp pebble, that unpleasant bit of information is just as clear and vivid when it arrives in your brain as it was at the start of its long upward journey.

Fortunately for us there is a mechanism, still not clearly understood, which permits us to adapt to certain types of continued stimuli. If you hold your left arm in your right hand, the stimulus provided by the pressure of your hand remains, but after a while you no longer notice your hand. This is not due to nerve fatigue, for if you release your hand and then reapply it, you will once again be notified of what has happened. Commonly we say we have "gotten used to" a particular change in the environment, and happily we are not at the mercy of an unchecked sensory input; otherwise we would wear ourselves out feeling our clothing, and we would never get more than our toes into the chilly ocean, which always feels much colder on first contact. This faculty of adaptation is essentially the genius of the nervous system.

Junctions

Conduction paths in the nervous system are made up of chains of neurons, but these nerve cells do not touch each other. Impulses going from the nerve endings of one nerve to another must bridge a gap, or junction, which is called a *synapse* (Fig. 10). How the impulse is transmitted across the synapse is still not fully understood. The transmission may be electrical, but we also know that there are certain chemical substances—such as acetylcholine—liberated by the endings of the first neuron, which play a role in bridging the synaptic junction.

Since there is always a slight delay at the synaptic junction, the speed of the traveling impulse is decreased according to the number of synapses it must cross. The synapse acts as a valve, or a switch, regulating the flow of nerve impulses and helping to maintain one-way traffic. Actually, when a nerve is exposed experimentally and stimulated anywhere but at its end points, it can conduct impulses in two directions,

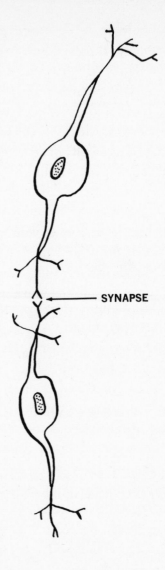

SYNAPSE

Fig. 10 *Synaptic junction between two neurons*

but in the body this does not generally occur. Local conditions determine whether an impulse has permission to cross the synaptic gap or whether it must wait for further impulses which will increase or decrease the strength of the message. Its path may even be blocked by an order to yield the right of way to other impulses arriving by different routes at the same junction. Thus fingers about to uncurl and drop a sizzling hot dish continue to hold tight—at least for a few seconds—upon receiving a message that the dish is glass, its contents liquid, and the rug waiting. The electrical properties of the junction, the presence of chemicals such as acetylcholine, the oxygen supply, fatigue, certain poisons and drugs, as well as habit, all play baffling roles in determining the patterns of nerve traffic.

Actually it is not quite this simple, for ultimately the brain decides what is relevant and what is not; yet were our synapses to forward every stimulus received, the person at the mercy of such indiscriminate gate-keepers would be extremely jumpy or "nervous." By the same principle it is believed that when we form a habit, we "break in" a set of nerve connections. Tying a shoelace for the first few times is an extremely complicated act. By the time we do it automatically, the shoe-lace-tying nerve paths are probably a well-worn route with a "green light" at each of the synapses.

Thus the synaptic junction is not an obstacle to the rapid transmission of impulses; rather, it provides an important clue to the physiological mechanism behind human behavior. Since all nerve impulses are electrical stimuli, and since the actual number of neurons in the human brain does not seem to be the deciding factor, it is reasonable to suppose that the "climate" of the synaptic junction influences the fate of every nerve impulse and, in the long run, has much to say about the patterns of nerve traffic. It is possible that part of the secret of human behavior lies at the microscopic junctions in the brain where nerve does not quite touch nerve.

4

INPUT–OUTPUT

The Ground Plan

To a limited extent the nervous system resembles a
telephone network in which receptor organs correspond to the receiver, nerve fibers are the system's wires,
the spinal cord its main cable, and the brain the central
exchange. The spinal cord is not only a relay center for
the endless stream of impulses traveling to the brain
but it contains substations capable of handling simple
reflex transactions without aid from higher levels and,
when required, notifying central headquarters of what
has been done. In a six-foot man, the spinal cord is
about three feet long and is crowned by the brain
which, like a huge mushroom, has engulfed the upper
part of its stalk, the ancient *brain stem* now contained
within the skull.

The brain and the spinal cord are called the *central
nervous system*. The nerves which run out to the body
from the central nervous system, although by no means
a separate system, are, for the sake of convenience, referred to as the *peripheral nervous system*.

The routes from the brain and spinal cord to the

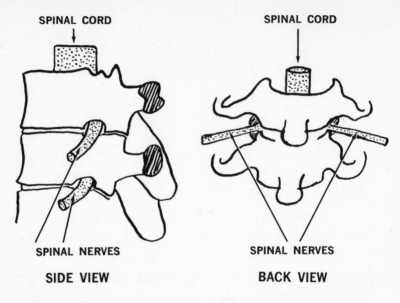

SPINAL CORD

SPINAL CORD

SPINAL NERVES

SPINAL NERVES

SIDE VIEW

BACK VIEW

Fig. 11 *Two views of spinal nerves as they emerge from the openings between vertebrae*

near and far reaches of the body are the cranial and spinal nerves. Twelve pairs of cranial nerves arise directly from the brain stem, and thirty-one pairs of spinal nerves emerge from openings on either side of the bony vertebrae of the spinal column (see Fig. 11). From there they divide and subdivide until every part of the body is enmeshed in a fine-spun web of nervous tissue. It is pressure on one of these large nerves by a spinal vertebrae whose cushion is defective which causes the severe pain of a slipped disc.

Without the skull to hold it together, the moist, rubbery brain would lose its familiar shape. The cortex of the bulging cerebrum is deeply wrinkled, or convoluted, while parallel and curved furrows divide the smaller cerebellum into leaves that resemble the sections of a tangerine. This is nature's ingenious answer to the problem of how to pack approximately three and a half square feet of valuable brain surface into an area five to six inches in diameter. A deep cleft, running from front to back, divides the cerebrum into left and right halves. These are known as the *cerebral hemispheres*. Each of the hemispheres is divided by other crevices which produce the four familiar lobes of the cerebral landscape—*frontal, temporal, parietal,* and *occipital* (Fig. 12).

The right cerebral hemisphere, always informed of what its partner is doing, controls movements made on the left side of the body, and similarly the left hemisphere governs the right side of the body. How this strange situation came to be remains one of evolution's puzzles, but as a result it is necessary for many of the "wires" to cross from one side of the central nervous system to the other. Generally this occurs in the brain stem and in the spinal cord.

To protect them from injury, the brain and spinal cord are wrapped in three membranes, the *meninges,* and then encased in bone. The nerve cells and their delicate tendrils are themselves supported by non-nervous connective tissue called the *neuroglia,* whose cells interlace to form a dense network between neurons.

As a final precaution the brain and spinal cord are

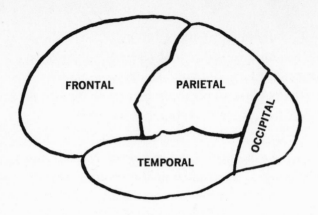

Fig. 12 *Side view of cerebral hemisphere showing four lobes*

cushioned by the *cerebrospinal fluid*, which protects the central nervous system from sudden shock and jarring. In composition somewhat like blood, from which it is derived, the colorless cerebrospinal fluid circulates through the four ventricles which are the connecting cavities within the brain. From the ventricles the fluid passes into the space between the two inner meninges and flows around the surface of the brain and spinal cord, eventually being reabsorbed into the blood stream. The complete function of the cerebrospinal fluid is not too well understood, yet changes in its pressure and chemical composition provide an important diagnostic tool for physicians who suspect disorders of the nervous system.

Every minute, one and a half pints of blood flow through the brain. Recently a clue to the riddle of genius has been sought in the blood supply to the brain. There is some evidence that the arteries of gifted people may be larger in diameter and therefore bring a greater volume of blood to the brain. The inference is that the more generous the blood bath, the better the brain cells can function.

Although its mechanism is still unknown, cerebral blood flow, unlike the blood supply to other organs, remains remarkably constant. The brain has actually been described as a bloodthirsty, insatiable vampire. Its blood flow is affected neither by eating nor by intellectual effort. Exercise, which makes the body's muscles greedy for blood, causes only a slight decrease in blood flow to the brain, while in sleep there is a small increase in its blood supply. Unfortunately the walls of the blood vessels which go through the central part of the brain are among the weakest in the body. If blood pressure within the vessels becomes too high or if the vessels themselves become brittle, they may burst, causing the hemorrhage and paralysis which we associate with a stroke. All the highly specialized cells of the human body depend on the circulating blood to provide the nourishment they require and to remove their waste products. The constancy of the cerebral blood supply guarantees reliable delivery of the two products on which the brain desperately depends: oxygen and glucose. It may be its greatest weakness, but the brain can endure little meddling with this vital supply.

Although the body can accumulate extra supplies of other vital nutrients, including water, it has no way to store oxygen. Because oxygen is ordinarily present in the air, a storage system seems to have been unnecessary. The gray matter of the brain is extremely sensitive to a decrease in oxygen, however, and will not gracefully tolerate a reduction in this precious commodity. Mental confusion and finally unconsciousness are the results of a decrease in the brain's oxygen quota—the fate of mountain climbers caught unequipped at high altitudes. It is estimated that eight minutes of total oxygen deprivation is enough to produce irreparable damage in certain of the brain's nerve cells.

Glucose, the form in which sugar circulates in the blood, is also urgently needed by the brain. A substantial drop in the blood sugar level may be a prelude to disaster. Mental confusion, muscular incoordination, convulsions, and loss of consciousness are the possible consequences. The role of glucose in the brain's nutrition is certainly dramatic, yet, curiously, it seems to have little to do with the fueling of mental effort. The extra calories needed for one hour of intense mental effort could be supplied by eating half a salted peanut. It is believed that poisons, anesthetics, and drugs affect the brain by interfering physically with a vital process —for example, the maintenance of the brain's oxygen supply or the conversion of glucose to energy.

Being and Doing

Thus far we have surveyed the basic equipment of the nervous system. Before we examine this system at work, however, it will be helpful to understand the kinds of human activity it is required to govern. If we consider function rather than structure, the nervous system can be divided into the so-called *voluntary* nervous system and the *autonomic*, or involuntary, nervous system. The voluntary nervous system supplies nerves to striped muscles—the muscles which move the skeletal parts. The autonomic nervous system sends its nerves to the glands and smooth muscles of the internal organs and blood vessels. It is the basic maintenance system of the body, to which is entrusted the almost automatic control of our internal organs. We shall consider this faithful branch more carefully in Chapter 6.

What are the duties of the voluntary nervous system, and is it truly voluntary? This is the division which manages those muscles capable of performing acts at our command and of which we are aware. It is the motor branch of the voluntary system with which we raise our arms, turn our heads, and chew our food.

We are not even conscious, however, of many of the movements for which this system is responsible, and others can be controlled only by a supreme effort. The difficulty of preventing yourself from blinking for any extended period of time or of remaining relaxed despite the pain of the dentist's drill make clear the apparently involuntary nature of some of the responses controlled by the voluntary nervous system. The inborn muscular responses called *reflexes* are usually beyond our control, and we are no more aware of them than we are of those reflexes which come under the jurisdiction of the unassuming autonomic nervous system. Pulling a hand away from a hot radiator, sneezing, coughing, or contracting the pupil of the eye in a bright light are common examples of reflex acts. When the doctor taps the patellar tendon below your knee cap with his hammer, the muscles which normally extend the knee contract and the leg jerks upward. This is a simple illustration of the many important and silent stretch reflexes of which we are ordinarily unaware. These reflexes maintain muscle tone and assure that every time a muscle is stretched it will also contract, so that the posture and balance of the body are maintained no matter how we bend, sway, jiggle, or jolt.

In addition to inherited reflex acts, there are also *conditioned reflexes* whose pathways are formed only after a period of training. These reflexes depend on the highest levels of the brain. In a famous experiment the celebrated physiologist Pavlov rang a bell every time a dog was fed. Soon the mere sound of the bell, without the presence of the actual food, was enough to cause the dog to salivate, for the animal had learned to associate the sound of the bell with the arrival of food.

In our daily lives we perform many complicated, learned acts which have in time become automatic. These acts are undoubtedly based on conditioned reflexes. Although the baby must turn his attention to the serious task of walking, it soon becomes an activity which proceeds automatically. After sufficient practice we can play the piano, typewrite, and drive cars without giving a conscious thought to the mechanics of what we are doing. Frequently we perform these acts better without conscious interference. A skilled typist will quickly tangle her fingers if she begins to "think" about what her fingers are doing. And although it is safe to dream about faraway places while running down a flight of stairs, it is not necessarily safe to think about the relationship between the steps and your feet. This does not mean that once a skill is acquired it is removed from higher control and delegated to a lower level in the nervous system. For example, if an injury occurs to the appropriate center in the cerebral cortex, the ability to walk is lost.

Discovery → *Integration* → *Change*

We may now ask: How does the voluntary nervous system work? What are the channels traveled by nerve impulses when we feel or move or when a muscle contracts? It is staggering to imagine the fantastically busy traffic in our nervous system, yet this traffic is orderly. If we understand the basic nerve circuit as illustrated by the reflex arc, we can build upon this model to construct still more subtle and intricate sensorimotor patterns.

Human behavior is transacted on the two great arms of the nervous system, the one sensory, the other motor, which form a circuit leading from "discovery" to "change." This route is often the body's private affair and need not be traveled at the level of consciousness. We are not generally aware of the sensory information coming from muscles and tendons, nor do we perceive the slight muscular responses with which the body maintains its balance and position. Even in a movement as consciously directed as reaching for your pen, it is only the movement which the cortical or conscious brain wills. You are completely unaware of the

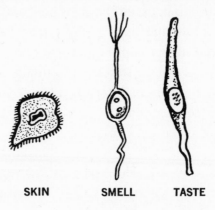

SKIN   SMELL   TASTE

Fig. 13   *Typical receptor endings*

many pairs of muscles which must cooperate to perform this act.

The "discovery" branch of the circuit begins with a *receptor*, either a specialized cell located at the end of a sensory nerve or the naked ending itself (see Fig. 13). The body's information services are in the hands of three kinds of receptor organs: News of the outside world is received by *exteroceptors* located in the special sense organs—eye, ear, nose, and tongue—as well as throughout the envelope which contains us, the skin.

Reports on the internal state of affairs are supplied by *interoceptors*, located in the internal organs and the walls of the blood vessels, and *proprioceptors*, located in the inner ear and buried in the muscles, tendons, and joints of the body.

The proprioceptors are interesting, for they provide us with our important self-senses. Sensitive to pressure, vibration, and to the position of the body and its parts in space, they indicate the tension of our muscles and the degree and direction of their movements. It is not necessary for us to be conscious of this information, but unless the central nervous system is well informed of the local state of affairs in its outlying muscles, it cannot begin to coordinate the movements of the hundreds of pairs of muscles necessary to maintain posture and balance, let alone to perform the formidable task of turning us into dancers, musicians, and people who eat with knives and forks.

Although traditionally we speak of "five senses"—vision, hearing, smell, taste, and touch—it becomes apparent that the curious "sixth sense" about which we timidly wonder needs a new rank assigned to it. The truth is that there are *numerous* senses, such as pain, light pressure, cold, and warmth, as well as the inner self-senses, including deep pressure, and muscle tension and vibration, which are concerned with the equilibrium, position, and posture of the body. We must not confuse a large sense organ such as the eye or ear with its microscopic receptor organs.

Each of the five special senses is actually composed of a variety of sensations provided by several receptors. Vision is a collective sense involving, in man, perception and depth. The taste of a great chef's masterpiece or of the most horrid medicine depends specifically upon four different taste receptors—those for salt, sweet, sour, and bitter sensations. The sense of touch is actually just one part of the important cutaneous (skin) senses, which include touch, cold, warmth, and pain.

A special word must be said at this point about pain, for it is perhaps one of the most fascinating and puzzling of our experiences. We still know too little about its mechanism and are too often victims of its special tyranny. Yet, paradoxically, we depend on this sensation to protect us from harm and destruction.

The sensation of pain is served by fine, unsheathed nerve filaments located near the surface of the skin, in the cornea of the eye, and within the body. Pain endings in the skin respond to a variety of stimuli which, at lower levels of intensity, may be experienced as touch, heat, cold, or pressure. When the stimulus becomes sufficiently intense, however, when it appears that tissue is actually in danger of being destroyed, the sensation becomes painful, usually retaining a component of the original sensation so that we know we are being burned and not pinched. We do not adapt to painful stimuli as we do, for example, to the ordinary warmth of our bath water. Should the water

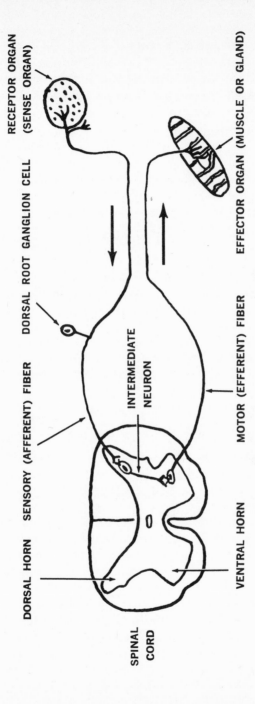

Fig. 14 A three-cell spinal reflex arc (Thicker arrows indicate direction in which impulse is transmitted.)

be hot enough to scald, we will never become accustomed to it. The sensation of pain may even persist long after we have hurriedly removed ourselves from the painful stimulus.

Having paused to survey the important receptor organs, let us now trace the complete route of the reflex arc. When stimulated appropriately, the receptor sets up an impulse which is carried by a sensory (afferent) neuron to the central nervous system. The actual cell body of the afferent neuron lies outside of the spinal cord in what is called the *dorsal root ganglion*. The dendrites of the sensory neuron synapse with those of the motor neuron in the gray matter of the spinal cord. With this, the "change" arm of the circuit begins. The motor neuron, whose cell body is found right within the spinal cord, conducts the impulse from the central nervous system out to an *effector organ*, a muscle which, alerted, now performs (see Fig. 14) .

It is tempting to assign our muscles to their own system and to refuse them admission to the rather exclusive nervous system, but nerve and muscle remain closely tied, as they have been since their earliest appearance. Muscle without nerve is usually paralyzed, but nerve without its servant muscle is completely useless.

These are the component parts of the simplest reflex arc, such as the knee jerk reflex. In most cases the route from discovery to change is intercepted by a central integrator either in a small office in the spinal cord or

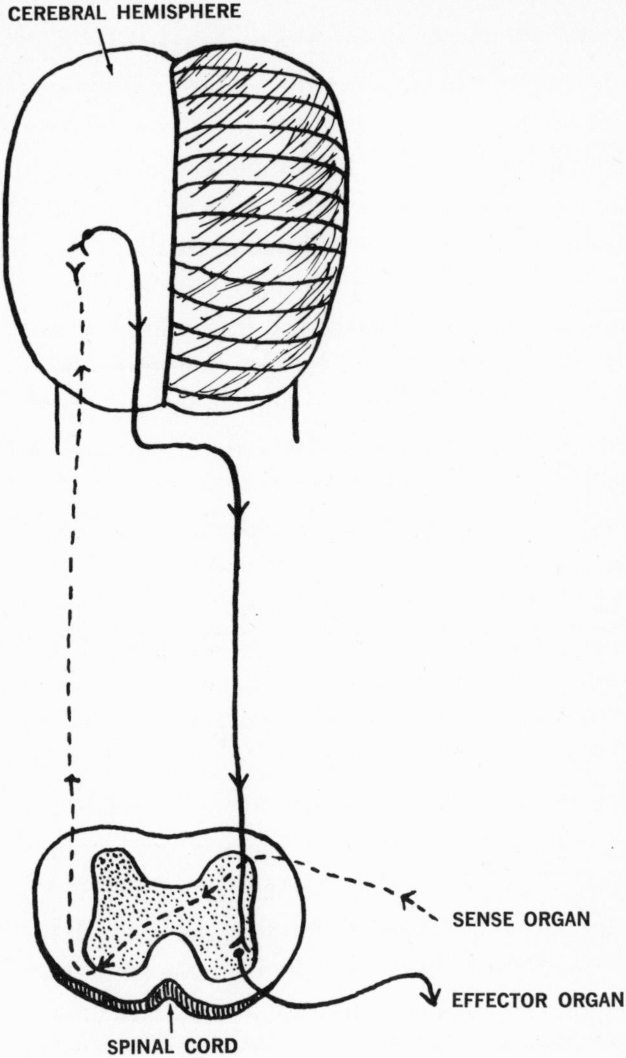

Fig. 15 *Schematic drawing of sensorimotor circuit going through the brain (Dotted line shows sensory route. Solid line shows motor route.)*

at central headquarters in the brain (see Fig. 15). The integrator's role is to sort the sensory information, decide upon its further distribution, and choose the appropriate channels to complete the response. Although the knee jerk reflex requires only a sensory and a motor neuron, this is unusual. Actually, as the body functions, there is no such thing as a "simple reflex." Other spinal reflexes involve at least a single intermediate neuron which lies in the gray matter of the spinal cord and links the sensory and motor arms (see Fig. 14). Despite the complex social behavior of insects, such as the ant and the bee, it is the simplicity of their integrating apparatus, their lack of a true brain, and their dependence on inflexible, inborn nerve pathways which restrict the behavior of insects to a series of automatic, self-triggering acts. Except in badly written science fiction these industrious creatures are not likely to challenge man's intellectual supremacy.

Patterns of Response

Now we must use our imagination and realize that apart from the simple scheme of diagrams, the nerve routes, which provide the physiological basis of human behavior, are vastly complicated, interlocking, and interrelated. The single stimulus of a sharp tack under your bare foot may result in an order delivered to many motor neurons and may involve a highly complicated pattern of muscular response, not to speak of the cortical response performed by the particularly human, thinking part of the brain.

Let us then step on a tack and observe, in far less time than it takes to read, the remarkable range of human behavior from an urgent flexion reflex to some higher consideration of the appropriate resting place for unemployed thumbtacks.

In response to painful stimulation of the skin of the sole of your foot a sensory nerve carries the information to the spinal cord, where it synapses with an intermediate neuron. The intermediate neuron, in turn, delivers the impulse to a motor neuron, which causes a flexor muscle in your leg to contract. Before you have time to "think about it," the leg bends at the knee and is promptly removed from the source of pain. This type of reflex is ancient in origin and has priority over other reflexes, for it protects the organism from harm. The flexion reflex is accompanied by another reflex which straightens the opposite leg at the knee, so that as you momentarily stand on one foot, you do not fall. At the same time, other motor neurons will probably notify the muscles which extend your arm and dictate other delicate shifts in balance to the many pairs and groups of muscles which must cooperate if you are to remain erect.

All of this occurs before you actually feel the pain. In order for pain to rise to the level of consciousness, the impulse from the sole of your foot not only triggers the spinal reflex arc but discharges other impulses in sensory neurons which carry the message up the sensory tracts of the spinal cord to an area in the brain known as the *thalamus*. Now, relatively long after your injured foot has been withdrawn, you are at last aware of pain. The thalamus is not the last step, however. Although this probably oversimplifies the complex relationship between the thalamus and its master, the *cerebral cortex*, it is only when the impulse reaches the cortex at the top of the brain that the crude pain information is further graded so that we know its severity and its source.

Now that you know you have stepped on a tack and hurt yourself, another series of responses follows. For example, the motor nerves running to the facial muscles may cause your face to grimace with pain, and unless you are of a stoic nature another volley of motor impulses will cause you to produce a resounding "Ouch!"

Next you may decide to pick up the offending tack so that the accident will not be repeated. But before you do this, you need more information—the location of the tack and of your hand. The silent proprioceptors keep you informed of your hand's position. Electrical impulses coming from the tack stimulate receptors in the retina of the eye, then travel over the optic nerve to the visual center in the brain so that you see it. Other information concerning the tack's position and its distance from you is also necessary before you succeed in executing the complicated movement which brings your hand swiftly and directly to the tack.

The total behavior pattern which began with a discharge of demanding impulses from the sole of your foot, answered promptly by a flexion reflex, is intricate and involved. It includes reflexes which adjust the body to its new position, a series of voluntary motor acts initiated by the conscious appreciation of what has happened, the use of additional sensory information, and, above all, a complicated tangle of memory, association, and decision. It is quite a performance.

"The Enchanted Loom"

In order to understand the nervous system, we have taken the convenient step of comparing it to a telephone network, examining its receiving and transmitting equipment and peering briefly into its circuits. But just as we were careful not to accept the nerve impulse too literally as a message, we must not carry the analogy of the telephone too far. The human nervous system is much wiser and far more flexible than any rigid telephone network in which the same combination of numbers automatically rings a bell in the same house. If smoke should stimulate the receptors in your nostrils, the fate of the message is still not predictable. Your brain may very well register the stimulus, and you will smell smoke, but another stimulus, such as the contents of a good mystery story, may inhibit the interpretation of the smoke data. Furthermore, whether you begin to salivate or place a hurried call to the fire department will depend on whether other nerve routes inform your brain that there is a steak on the broiler or the house is on fire.

Sir Charles Sherrington, the father of modern neurology and in a way the poet of the nervous system, once brilliantly described the brain as ". . . an enchanted loom where millions of flashing shuttles weave a dissolving pattern, always a meaningful pattern, though never an abiding one." The patterns and subpatterns vary with the total equilibrium of the body. Even an action as simple as reaching for your pen will depend upon the original position of your arm and body in relation to the pen. It is the task of the brain and its subordinate stations to see that impulses speeding along peripheral lines, climbing up the tracts of the spinal cord, weaving dense patterns in the fiber of the brain itself, make proper connections in which the demands of the inner body and of the immediate outer environment, as well as the increasingly complex demands of human society, are integrated in significant and appropriate behavior.

5

CENTRAL HEADQUARTERS

Inside the Skull

Although the brain is not impressive in appearance, we cannot help but regard it with awe and wonder. For this curious moist package is the anatomical home of a human being's most human qualities: his personality, his thoughts, his fears and hopes, and his talents. Yet long as we stare at this brain, even if we probe its interior, we shall not know whether we hold the brain of a genius or a fool, nor shall we find in it goodness and mercy, memory and imagination, or the trail of an evil life. Nevertheless the fleeting electrical patterns of the dynamic, living brain have supplied veiled hints of the brain's private life. It is probable that these secrets lie hidden in the physical and chemical mysteries of its impressionable and responsive cells.

As an organ of the body the human brain is unique in one respect, for it is the only organ which has discovered itself. Despite its regal powers, however, the brain is not a sovereign superstructure living on its own terms but is subject to the rules of the body, the organization to which it belongs. As an organ the brain is efficient yet demanding, vulnerable and yet strangely sturdy. Although heir to certain old-age woes and literally at the mercy of its blood supply, it is not generally the brain which limits the number of our days.

Within the central executive there is a division of authority, and in order to understand the brain we must study the parts of which it is composed. It has become increasingly evident that these divisions are not independent of one another. The brain functions as a whole and is provided with such a wilderness of circular nerve routes that the cooperation of its parts is built into its fundamental design.

Nobody can construct a human brain. It has been estimated that to build even a crude model would require 1,000 billion billion tubes, an equal number of wires, a warehouse thirteen hundred times the size of an ordinary room, and at least a million kilowatts of electric power. Yet the human brain is comfortably installed in the head and runs on a mere fortieth of a kilowatt (25 watts).

Our brain is not the heaviest brain in the animal kingdom. The brains of the whale and the elephant surpass ours in absolute weight, but in proportion to their total body weight their brains weigh relatively less. Our brain is also not the largest organ in the body. That honor belongs to the liver. Recent studies have shown that the human brain, like other organs in the body, slowly shrinks after we reach maturity, losing approxi-

all very well to have a cerebrum, a cerebellum, even a thalamus, but who is to screen impulses before they are admitted to these higher offices? Who is to proclaim holidays and order overtime? It now appears that to the reticular formation is entrusted the vital role of arousing and activating the highest levels of the brain. If you stimulate the upper part of this area in a sleeping or drowsy animal, it will awaken. Disease of or injury to the reticular formation can lower the level of consciousness to the point of coma. Not unexpectedly it is sensitive to various chemicals, tranquilizers, and barbiturates. In an even more subtle capacity, one which is still poorly understood, the reticular formation seems to adjust the level of our attention, turning it up or down. It is possible that it does this by controlling the degree to which we are aware of sensory impulses streaming into our brain. There is even some indication that it may influence the original sensitivity of certain sense organs. Because of its location in the heart of the vital brain stem, it is difficult to study the reticular formation. Yet it is conceivable that this dense network of nerve cells will one day yield clues to some of the brain's least understood problems, including the nature of consciousness, sleep, attention, and the mechanism of hallucination.

It is risky and certainly unscientific to ascribe the social relationships of human beings to the parts of the human body, yet it is pleasing to know that the vener-

Fig. 18   **TABLE OF CRANIAL NERVES** (simplified)

Number	Name	Origin (or Terminal) in Brain	Principal Functions Sensory	Motor
I	Olfactory	Under side of frontal lobes of cerebrum	Smell	
II	Optic	Occipital lobes of cerebrum	Vision	
III	Oculomotor	Midbrain	Muscle sense	Movement of eyeball
IV	Trochlear	Midbrain	Muscle sense	Movement of eyeball
V	Trigeminal	Pons	Sensation in face and head, in eyes, nose, mouth and teeth	Movement of lower jaw
VI	Abducens	Pons	Muscle sense	Movement of eyeball
VII	Facial	Pons	Taste	Facial expression; salivation
VIII	Acoustic	Pons	Hearing; maintenance of equilibrium	
IX	Glosso-pharyngeal	Medulla	Taste; sensation in pharynx and tongue	Swallowing; salivation
X	Vagus	Medulla	Sensation in pharynx, larynx, trachea, and other thoracic and abdominal organs	Supplies muscles of pharynx, larynx, heart, and other thoracic and abdominal organs

Number	Name	Origin (or Terminal) in Brain	Principal Functions Sensory	Motor
XI	Spinal Accessory	Medulla; upper part of spinal cord		Supplies muscles of pharynx; movement of shoulder
XII	Hypoglossal	Medulla		Movement of tongue

able brain stem may no longer be relegated to the position of a mere superhighway with some admittedly vital but dull reflex duties. The discovery of the great significance of the reticular formation somehow preserves the dignity of the hard-working brain stem in the presence of its more sophisticated colleagues further up in the hierarchy of the brain.

Talking to Muscles

Attached to the rear of the brain stem so that it almost seems to be riding piggyback is a symmetrical structure known as the *cerebellum* (see Fig. 16). This organ consists of two hemispheres which surround a narrow, curved central stalk. The cerebellum has an interior consisting mostly of white matter and an outside mantle of gray matter called the *cerebellar cortex*.

Only one-sixth of this cortex actually appears on the surface. The rest is folded into slender parallel grooves which ridge the lobes of the organ.

In the eighteenth century the function of the cerebellum was so misunderstood that it was thought to be the seat of sexual impulses. Eventually physiologists removed the cerebellum of a pigeon and discovered that the bird's sexual impulses appeared unaffected, but it toppled over every time it tried to move, and when the bird attempted to fly, its wings could do no more than thrash aimlessly through the air. Today we know that the chief duty of the cerebellum is to coordinate and synchronize the performance of our muscles so that the movements we ultimately produce are steady, smooth, and efficient. These activities are carried out below the level of consciousness. The cerebellum's influence is not limited to its role as "muscle boss," for in some way still unknown it also participates in the coordination of the sensations of touch, sight, and hearing.

The cerebellum is a large administrative office under the executive control of the cerebral hemispheres. When its master, the cerebral cortex, issues an order to raise your arm, it is the cerebellum which mobilizes the required muscle forces and determines the exact amount of muscle pull needed to perform complex movements in which there is almost the same amount of action in opposing muscles.

Injury to the human cerebellum does not result in

paralysis but, instead, in a loss of harmony among the many elements of muscular activity. Without the regulation of the cerebellum, movements are no longer smooth and precise. They become jerky, clumsy, and inaccurate and easily break down into their component parts. The force of a given movement will no longer be in proportion to the work it must do: A hand reaching for a spoon not only misses the mark but lurches and jerks as it extends in stages. A hand grasping a tennis racket can no longer count on the appropriate muscles of the arm to contract simultaneously and "fix" the wrist, elbow, and shoulder joints so that the racket can be held in the desired position.

In certain cases the cerebellum is capable of truly remarkable performances. Of all the movements we make, those of the hand are the most skilled and complicated. An accomplished pianist can play fairly difficult music at the rate of twenty to twenty-five notes per second, a feat which for the ten fingers alone may require four hundred to five hundred separate motor actions, not counting the movements of the wrists, arms, shoulders, and legs.

To do its job effectively the cerebellum requires a complex system of communication for both incoming and outgoing impulses. A circular route going through the pons to the cerebral hemispheres makes it possible for the cerebellum to receive orders from above and at the same time to report back to its "chief." In addition it has extensive connections, not yet fully explored, with the brain stem, particularly with the reticular formation. And at all times sensory nerves from muscles and joints, the middle ear, and the five external sense organs keep the cerebellum informed of the state of the body's muscles as well as the position of the parts of the body in space. Using this information, the cerebellum may then inform the cerebral cortex of adjustments to be made in its final instructions or may itself issue swift, integrated orders to muscles located throughout the body. In this way the ingredients of movements are blended to produce precise and effective results.

Anatomically beautiful, complex, and extensive in its influence, the cerebellum is understandably called the "little brain." And yet it is not a brain—certainly not in the sense that it can capture and hold an image so that it may forever reflect on it. The cerebellum is what engineers call a *servomechanism*. It is a high-powered administrator which regulates the performance of work planned and ordered elsewhere.

Junior Executives

In the evolution of lower animals the *thalamus* and *hypothalamus* were the forerunners of the powerful executive system which only later developed with the overflowing of the cerebral cortex. Today these structures are overshadowed and dominated by the massive hemispheres which rise above them. They remain, nevertheless, the ground floor of the brain's executive division and are the level at which impulses may first become conscious.

The thalamus, which means "inner chamber," is a large oval mass of nerve cells divided into two lobes. It lies above the midbrain and is buried between the cerebral hemispheres. The thalamus serves as a great sensory way station where impulses headed for the cerebral cortex are intercepted and crudely sorted. As a sensory receiving station the thalamus is a primitive center, for the statements it makes about sensation are general and uncritical. For example, the thalamus may know that an object is touching the body, but the cerebral cortex must participate before we know the exact part of the body involved and whether a warm object is a radiator or a hot-water bottle.

The human thalamus is concerned with the manufacture of a rather general product called "feeling tone." To this ancient structure we owe, in part, our vague awareness of well-being, of general comfort or discomfort. The thalamus is also the first receiving station for visual and auditory impulses, and it is here that painful stimuli first become conscious. It is believed to be involved in the phenomena of wakefulness and sleep and therefore in the ultimate mystery of consciousness. There may also be an area in the thalamus in which sensations from our internal organs become crudely conscious. Furthermore, there is some evidence that it may be one of the many structures involved in the creation of our sense of time, perhaps even in the memory of past and recent events. And, most important, it forms, with the hypothalamus, part of the primitive seat of emotional expression.

As the brain evolved in the human direction, the sensory functions of the thalamus apparently were brought under the domination of the cerebral cortex. Perhaps some of the most fascinating information about the true nature of the thalamus has come from the study of individuals and animals in whom the thalamic connections with the cortex are damaged, so that the thalamus escapes from the inhibiting control of its master and, unbridled, is left to deal out sensation in its raw form. It is a bad business when, due to injury or disease, crude sensation is allowed to run riot: The prick of a needle may not even be perceived at normal levels of intensity. At higher levels, however, it may explode as an ill-defined sensation, so unpleasant and painful that it is intolerable. The individual's response to this stimulus therefore appears to be excessive, even bizarre. Such a person may drop a glass of ice water rather than suffer the pain of holding it. Men have been known to grow beards to avoid the excruciating pain of shaving. And the sound of music may cause intense bodily discomfort, even in people who ordinarily enjoy music.

If the role of the thalamus is impressive, that of the tiny hypothalamus is even more remarkable. This small body, only three hundredths of the total brain weight, is located beneath the thalamus and therefore lies at the base of the cerebrum. Hanging by a stalk from the undersurface of the hypothalamus is the powerful *pituitary gland*. This gland is often called the "master gland" because it secretes hormones which, in turn, regulate other endocrine glands of the body. The part of the pituitary gland which is near the hypothalamus is actually derived from embryonic brain tissue, and at this point there appears to be a significant holding of hands between the two regulating divisions of the body—the nervous and the endocrine systems.

The hypothalamus is the central organ for the control of the autonomic nervous system. Strategically located at the junction of the central and autonomic nervous systems and the endocrine system, the hypothalamus is involved in some of the most fundamental of the body's reactions, including sleep, sexual activity, sugar and fat metabolism, temperature and water regulation, and appetite control. Moreover it is the center which coordinates many important processes—the pounding heart, the dry mouth and sweaty palms— by which the body expresses emotion.

The relationship between the hypothalamus and its overlord, the cerebrum, has long fascinated investigators studying the emotions. Most of the experiments performed so far have involved animals, and there is a danger in implying that what is true for a dog or cat is also the case for a human being, whose brain may no longer retain the more primitive relationships found even in higher animals.

If you stimulate the appropriate portion of an animal's hypothalamus or, as recently discovered, if you deprive it of the control of the ancient smell-brain in the cerebral hemispheres, you can produce an artificial condition known as "sham rage." Upon the slightest provocation the experimental animal will bite, claw, and struggle furiously. The pupils of its eyes will dilate, its hair will stand on end, and its blood pressure will rise. In fact the animal displays the signs of extreme emotion we might expect in a normal animal which has just cause to be angered or frightened. It would appear that in normal animals and possibly in human beings the free-wheeling enthusiasm of the hypothalamus is adjusted by higher centers in the brain so that these basic responses are restricted to appropriate occasions and even then are suitably modified.

A Small Puzzle

Before we advance to the top floor of the brain and at last consider the twin hemispheres which rule the cerebral castle, the curious *pineal body* must be mentioned. The pineal body—a small mass of non-nervous tissue shaped like a pine cone—is located above the midbrain between the two lobes of the thalamus. This organ, known for at least two thousand years, was at one time thought to regulate the flow of thought. In the seventeenth century it was designated by Descartes, the renowned French philosopher and mathematician, as the seat of the soul. Eventually it was toppled from its lofty throne and came to be considered a mere rudimentary structure with little or no use—a view still held by many people. But the pineal gland also has devoted champions who claim that it is a useful although admittedly puzzling gland belonging to the endocrine system.

The Twin Rulers

The cerebrum is the organ of learning, of choice, of prediction, and of inhibition. The human brain, with its giant cerebral hemispheres, is born with fewer prior commitments than the brain of any other species. Flexible and uncommitted, the cerebrum is the true organ of autobiography. Nevertheless the "organ of the mind," the physical residence of personality, remains a businesslike center with the nervous system's old-fashioned obligation of linking sensation and movement, but this time at the highest level of integration.

The cerebral hemispheres are two pouchlike structures which, rather than crowning the rest of the brain, have flopped over and engulfed it (see Fig. 16). They are joined by several bands, or bridges, of white fibers. Between them lies the thalamus. In right-handed people the left hemisphere is generally a little heavier, and it is interesting that the cerebral area which governs the muscles of speech is found in the larger and dominant hemisphere. Theories have been proposed that speech may have evolved in the service of a skillful, inquiring hand.

The cerebrum contains an estimated ten billion nerve cells, which are lodged mostly in the thin, gray cortex. Even at its thickest part the cortex measures no more than three-eighths of an inch. Only one-third of this thin rind actually appears on the surface. The rest is buried in the finger-like convolutions. Although the brains of higher animals are definitely more convoluted than those of their relatives lower on the evolutionary scale, the furrowing of the human brain cannot be directly linked to intelligence. As in other species, the convolutions of all human brains are arranged in similar patterns, and so far no one has discovered any significance in the slight variations among the brains of human beings.

If you cut through the cortex into the interior of one of the hemispheres, you will see first the gray rind and then the white matter, which consists of several kinds of nerve fibers: those which provide communication within the hemisphere itself, as well as the fiber bridges which unite the two hemispheres.

Buried within the white fibers of the cerebral hemispheres are several distinct clumps of gray matter, some as large as a hen's egg. These collections of nerve cells are known by the rather loose term *basal ganglia*. They are an ancient heritage and have considerable authority in lower vertebrates, whose cerebral hemispheres are still small. As the hemispheres ballooned about the primitive brain, these masses of gray matter were buried in the center. Here, intimately connected with

parietal lobe, lies the general sensory area (see Fig. 19). Actually the two areas overlap, an illustration of structural common sense, for it is almost impossible to conceive of movement without its partner sensation. In the sensory cortex, primary sensations are evaluated critically. It is here that a pin prick is differentiated from a knife cut and localized on the tip of your finger. It is here that the comparisons "warmer than" or "colder than" are formulated.

The body is represented in these sensorimotor areas in such a way that its true anatomical proportions are ignored. Instead cortical space is assigned the various parts of the body according to the extent to which we are aware of them and according to our ability to manipulate them consciously. The skillful hand receives a proportionately higher share of cortical real estate, with the thumb and index fingers enjoying top priority. The motor cortex "knows" the forearm and hand, leg and foot, as practical, functional units created by the joints, although this is not the way the actual nerves are distributed to these areas. If you close your eyes and let your hand hang at your side, you will be clearly aware of the presence of your thumb and index finger, but unless you yield to temptation and move them, the remaining fingers tend to run together in a blur. Of your toes, only the big toe seems to have a separate identity, but its personality is colorless when compared to its counterpart in the hand.

In addition to the general sensorimotor areas, other sensory and motor territories have been mapped out in the cortex (see Fig. 19). Hearing has been localized in the temporal lobes. We see with the back of the brain, at the pole of the occipital lobes. Smell and taste are located at the base of the cerebral hemisphere in the old smell brain. A recent discovery of great importance is that our somewhat antique smell brain is part of a complex system which includes certain other nerve cell groups as well as areas in the frontal lobes, and is sometimes referred to as the "visceral brain." Not only are these areas concerned with the regulation of our visceral, or internal, organs but, not surprisingly, they are involved in the physiology of emotion.

The cortical home of hunger and thirst, if it exists, still eludes us, although the latest experiments suggest that the hypothalamus may be partially responsible for the sensation of thirst. There seems to be no specific cortical area in which pain is registered. It is more likely that, as we have already seen, the primitive sensation of pain is experienced in the thalamus and that the sensory cortex is responsible for locating and grading the sensation. If regions of the frontal lobes are removed or if their connections with the thalamus are severed, we know that people suffering from severe pain experience a curious kind of relief. While the individual still feels the pain, he no longer suffers or seems to be concerned about it. Finally, there is no single area which can claim the glory of human speech, although the motor area which controls the muscles of speech is located in the frontal lobe of the dominant cerebral hemisphere.

The No-Man's Land

Large parts of the cortex have no specific motor or sensory functions. Known as the *association areas* and sometimes called "silent" because they respond least specifically to experimental prying, these perplexing, uncharted regions contain the secrets of the human brain we would most dearly like to possess. Responsive and adaptable, the association areas are the parts of the brain which finally contribute to the higher processes of mind. Here, in some unknown way, thought is created, personality emerges, and intelligence is sown. The frontal lobes contain important association areas, but neither intelligence nor any other mental capacity is limited to this region. They are probably the obligation of the entire cortex. The patterns of the human mind are woven throughout our lifetime and depend on such an immense and rich body of experience that it would be difficult to confine this vast tapestry to anything less than the entire cerebral cortex.

We do not know how the association areas function, yet in the dense forests of their nerve connections the highest integrative work of the brain is mysteriously accomplished. It is here that movement is given purpose and sensory information is forged into concepts which have meaning for us. Thus a round, orange-colored object is recognized as an "orange," and even if we close our eyes and rely solely on our senses of touch and smell, we still know we are holding an orange. The motor relationships of the association areas are similar. We can stimulate an area in the motor cortex experimentally and produce a movement, but intelligent, meaningful movements, the movements with which our hands reach for the orange and then peel it, require the guidance of the neurons of the association areas.

The cerebral cortex has been briefly described as the highest station for sensation and movement as well as the home base for our mental life. It is important to realize that just as we observed sensorimotor arcs in the spinal cord and at lower levels of the brain, so too we find them at the very roof of the brain. However, the complicated circuits, beginning in sensation and ending in movement, which loop through the cerebral cortex are of the most intricate and complex type. At a lower level of the nervous system the stimulus "hot" leads to the quick withdrawal of the hand even before the sensation becomes conscious. At the top of the brain, an orange perceived becomes, somewhat more slowly, an orange eaten—or not eaten.

Behind the Wheel

To observe the remarkable range of human behavior for which the brain is ultimately responsible—from the needs we share with a fish to those skills and attitudes which are uniquely human—let us consider ourselves as we drive a car. We take it for granted that our heart will beat seventy times a minute, that the lungs will serve loyally, that the alimentary canal will perform all the complex rites of digestion, and that the self-senses will tell us where to find our hands and legs. Eventually even the task of putting the car through its paces is reduced to a series of learned, automatic responses. Our color vision informs us that the light is green; through our ability to translate symbols we understand that it means "go," and we are sufficiently flexible to modify that rule if someone is blocking the way.

Driving along, we are also aware of our personal barometer—whether we are tired or rested, cheerful or worried, comfortable or uncomfortable. Against this subjective, inner background, while listening to music coming from the car radio, we may at the same time be contemplating the state of our finances or conversing with a friend. Finally, according to our understanding of the concepts of right and wrong and the rules of road courtesy, each time we sit behind the wheel of an automobile we are concerned with very much more than survival: We demonstrate those unique moral values which form the cream of our human heritage.

6

WITHOUT CONSULTING YOU

Man composes symphonies, he aims for the moon, he turns seed into cloth and probes the mysteries of life and the universe. Yet the material of which he is made is itself impermanent, and its basic components are not rare and marvelous substances but the common elements found on his planet. Since the greater part of this material is water, it is indeed a wonder that man does not evaporate on the first hot summer day.

We rarely stop to realize that protoplasm, the jelly-like substance of which every cell in the body is composed, is extremely unstable, and unless certain specific conditions are maintained, it quickly decomposes. Compared to nonliving things such as rocks and pots and pans, the length of time protoplasm can maintain its characteristic identity is relatively short, even under the most favorable circumstances.

The raw material of life consists of elements such as hydrogen, oxygen, carbon, nitrogen, phosphorus, and iron, found not only in living things but in nonliving things as well. These basic building blocks link hands and form larger compounds known as molecules. Water molecules account for 70 to 95 per cent of the cell. Molecules of carbohydrates, fats, proteins, nucleic acids, and inorganic salts such as ordinary table salt are other important ingredients of protoplasm.

'The task of extracting the incredibly complex secrets of cell life has become one of the major challenges of modern science. The living cell is not inert. It is a bustling chemical laboratory, a "magic hive" which in some way oversees the activity of its billions of dancing molecules, disposing of worn-out parts and manufacturing replacements, so that the cell retains its specific internal organization. For as long as the cell can do this, it lives. When its characteristic identity can no longer be maintained, when the balance between building and decomposition is upset, the cell breaks down into its simpler parts and ceases to be alive. Thus the meaning of life and death is contained in nothing so obvious as a beating heart nor even in the constituents of protoplasm but in the precarious physical and chemical equilibrium maintained within the walls of the industrious cell. The expression "life flows on" conveys a truth the cell has always known.

Cell settles next to cell to create tissues and organs. Inevitably cell societies are very specific in their requirements for suitable living conditions. Should the cells of our brain be deprived even briefly of the blood flow which delivers their vital supplies of oxygen and glucose, a protest is immediately registered and we faint. Drowning, electric shock, and gas poisoning leave no mark on the body, and yet they are swift killers because they interfere with the fundamental needs of cell life, violating its precarious internal organization.

So delicately balanced is the life of the body's tissues and so overwhelming are the internal and external dangers to which they are exposed that special precautions are necessary to maintain this vital equilibrium. It is startling to realize that if it were not immediately eliminated, the heat produced within our bodies by twenty minutes of maximum muscular effort would be sufficient to set the albuminous substances in the body like the white of a hard-boiled egg. Outside in the vast, shifting impersonal environment there are external dangers to which the human body can learn to adjust—extremes of heat and cold, the impoverished air of high altitudes, and at all times the armies of microscopic organisms waiting to enter and devour us.

Fortunately all living creatures possess, in varying degrees, a built-in "self-righting" mechanism which enables them to maintain a steady internal environment despite external threats and internal manufacturing hazards. Where this equipment is not so well refined, the animal's adaptation may be awkward. The frog must sleep the long winter through in the mud at the bottom of his pond, and the snake abruptly suspends activity to escape from daily extremes of temperature. Mammals are better equipped, and their most complex specimen, man, has made his more remarkable accommodations to nature, not as the result of a direct biological adaptation, but indirectly, by means of the inventions of the greatest of all biological gifts, the human brain. Day and night, in all seasons of the year, man ranges his planet from pole to pole, soars above it, and hunts not only its four-legged beasts but its microscopic inhabitants as well. That this is possible, that conditions permitted the development of man's cerebral "supertool" is due, however, to a profound biological truth observed by a great French physiologist in the nineteenth century. It was Claude Bernard who pointed out that an animal becomes free and independent of its external environment only to the extent that it has developed a mechanism for maintaining the steadiness of its internal environment.

As amazing as our body is, it has not yet achieved this ideal. The human body is by no means "free" of the world in which it lives; its internal climate is not perfectly maintained, nor is it as wise as it is commonly thought to be. Anyone who has suffered from an aching back knows that our bony scaffolding is not perfectly designed for the demands we make upon it. Healing processes which leave behind them a trail of scars frequently destroy the organ they set out to repair, and the margin of safety in biochemical adjustments is often less than comfortable. In spite of these imperfections, our ability to cope with the many hazards of living depends to a large extent on the remarkable efficiency of our interior housekeeping.

Maintenance and Adjustment

The coordination and control of this stabilizing mechanism is left largely to the *autonomic*, or *involuntary*, *nervous system*, which supplies nerves to our vital structures, conserves their resources, and helps them adjust to the pressures of the outside world. Without consulting you, this division speeds the heart and increases blood pressure when you are racing to catch a train. It is also the system which quietly restores the normal heart beat and blood distribution once you are safely aboard.

Most of the time the autonomic nervous system runs our internal organs automatically, without troubling us. Relieved of such humble but demanding duties as remembering to turn on the digestive system, directing the body's waste disposal, or pacing its beating heart, we are free to sleep undisturbed and safely or to organize interplanetary excursions. Perhaps this arrangement is a wise precaution, for it is not altogether certain that the control of the functions vital to life should be entrusted to those curious animals who lose pens, regard French fries and pizza as adequate nourishment, and insist upon transporting their all too human bodies to improbable places along the ocean floor and beyond the planet rim. On the other hand, it is just this freedom from the routine of daily housekeeping which has made it possible for man to invent pizza and fountain pens and to probe both outer space and his inner tissues.

The autonomic nervous system governs the activity of our glands and of the *smooth (unstriped) muscle* found in the walls of our internal organs and blood vessels, as well as of *cardiac muscle*, a variety found in the heart. This branch of our nervous system is purely a motor system; it includes neither the equally important sensory nerves which carry incoming messages from the internal organs nor the important sensory nerves of the voluntary system which bring information from the outside world and participate in voluntary as well as autonomic reflexes.

As if to emphasize its functional independence, part of the autonomic nervous system has migrated from the spinal cord and has moved out into the body, closer to the organs it controls. It is true that nerve fibers of the voluntary system travel long distances through the body, but their cell bodies remain at home in the spinal cord or brain. The nerve cell bodies of the autonomic system have actually left the home office and set up "field stations," called *ganglia* or *plexuses*, nearer the organs they manage and in some cases inside the very walls of these structures. One of these outposts is the vulnerable solar plexus, located in the abdomen. A sharp punch "below the belt" may strike this complicated plexus and trigger a series of reflexes which decrease the blood supply to the brain and produce loss of consciousness.

The autonomic system is by no means anatomically

free of the central nervous system, however, for even the most remote autonomic ganglia are strung by their nerve fibers to other autonomic neurons whose cell bodies lie within the spinal cord. The processes of these cells, in turn, go through the spinal cord to centers in the brain. And here originate the stories of a stomach which can be sabotaged by a brain, a blush which replies to a compliment, and a criminal whose lies are exposed by his innocent lungs and heart in the recordings of a lie detector.

Unlike the voluntary system, in which one motor nerve cell completes the entire journey from the exit in the spinal cord or brain to its muscle terminal, the equivalent motor arm in the autonomic nervous system consists almost always of at least a two-neuron chain. The cell body of the first neuron lies in the spinal cord. Its fibers run to a ganglion lying somewhere outside the central nervous system, where it synapses with a second neuron or set of neurons, whose axons then complete the outward route to organ, blood vessel, or gland.

Two Arms

Our involuntary nervous system consists of two great nerve trunks, known as the sympathetic and parasympathetic divisions. The spinal cord stations for the *sympathetic system* are limited to the cord's midsection and, like other nerve fibers leaving or entering the spinal cord, the sympathetic fibers emerge from the central cable through the spinal nerves. On both sides of the spinal cord there is a chain of twenty-one or twenty-two sympathetic ganglia which run from the base of the skull to the tip of the spine (see Fig. 20).

A typical sympathetic fiber emerges from the spinal cord and detours a short distance to a way station in a sympathetic ganglion. From here the fiber may go for an "elevator ride" up or down the string of sympathetic ganglia, "visiting" other levels before setting out on the long journey to destinations in the body. The first sympathetic neuron meets the second neuron in its two-neuron chain either in a sympathetic ganglion lying close to the spinal cord or in a collateral ganglion or plexus (see Fig. 21).

The spinal cord exits for *parasympathetic* nerve fibers are arranged like book ends with sympathetic stations contained between them. Parasympathetic fibers emerge through the cranial nerves of the midbrain and the medulla and through spinal nerves coming from the lowest portion of the spinal cord (see Fig. 20). Unlike the sympathetic system, these nerve fibers do not gather and intermingle in a chain of ganglia strung immediately outside the spinal cord. Instead they travel directly to their secondary ganglia stations, which lie closer to the organs they serve and are sometimes imbedded in their very walls (see Fig. 21).

One of the most distinguished of the parasympathetic nerves is the great tenth cranial nerve, the *Vagus*, which, unlike most of the other cranial nerves,

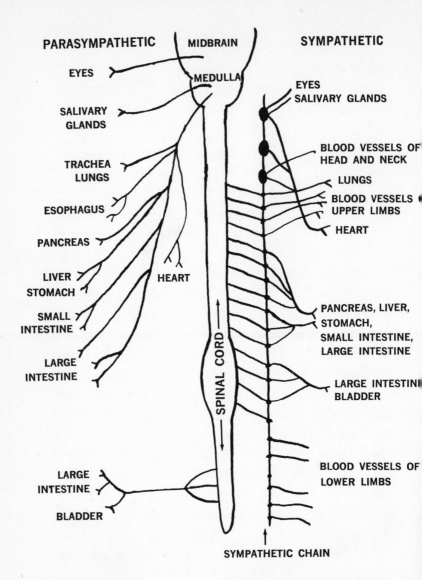

Fig. 20 *Diagram of the autonomic nervous system showing the relationship between the sympathetic and parasympathetic divisions and some of the organs innervated (Details of distribution are diagrammatic.)*

has business in areas other than the head. The Vagus (meaning "wanderer") drifts downward through the body to destinations in the heart and in the digestive and respiratory systems.

Dual Control

Once outside the central highway in the spinal cord, autonomic nerve fibers fan out until practically all the organs of the body receive a representative from both the sympathetic and parasympathetic systems (as shown in Fig. 20). The anatomy of our involuntary nervous system may at first glance seem unduly complicated, perhaps even strangely organized, yet we shall see that its anatomical design is beautifully suited for the antagonistic but coordinated roles both of its divisions play in regulating our vital life processes.

There are more exceptions, but in general the sympathetic system, like its brother, the core of the adrenal gland known as the *adrenal medulla*, mobilizes the body for emergency action and for strenuous activity. The parasympathetic system conserves the body's resources. The relationship between these two branches is diplomatic, for both systems, according to need, either excite or inhibit bodily activity.

When you swim or play basketball it is your sympathetic system which inhibits the activity of the stomach and intestines, constricts the blood vessels of the digestive tract so that more blood can be delivered to the lungs and skeletal muscles, speeds the heart

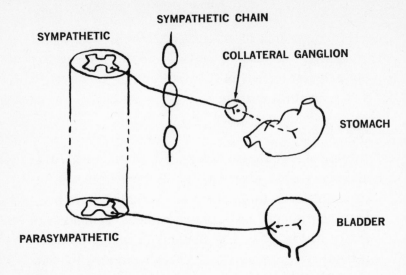

Fig. 21 *Schematic drawing of typical sympathetic and parasympathetic nerve supply to viscera*

beat, and increases fuel supplies by raising the blood sugar level. If you have just been frightened by a burglar, impulses carried by sympathetic nerves dilate the pupils of the eye, increase the secretion of sweat; and by contracting the smooth muscle in the skin they cause the hair to stand on end, which in relatively hairless man produces the rather useless response we recognize as "gooseflesh."

Once unusual external stress has passed, the parasympathetic system exerts its sobering influence: It constricts the pupils, inhibits sweating, slows the heart beat, lowers blood pressure, and restores the digestive mechanism as well as normal bodily metabolism. The duties of the parasympathetic system are not necessarily limited to checking its hot-tempered sympathetic companion, however. As the general protector of the body's resources it is intimately concerned with the constructive processes of digestion, reproduction, and elimination by which the body is prevented from choking to death on its own waste products.

With its direct routes to the organs of the body, the parasympathetic system exerts an influence which is specific and local; the sympathetic system, with its great ganglion chains in which sympathetic fibers intermingle before fanning out, produces the more widespread effects which prepare the body to meet the challenge of emergency and stress. The sympathetic system has been compared to the loud and soft pedals of a piano, which modulate all the notes at one time; the parasympathetic division more closely resembles the individual piano keys. Laboratory animals live and even reproduce if deprived of the sympathetic branch of their nervous system. However, they must be carefully protected and sheltered. Having lost the power to adjust to variations in outside temperature and to the demands of stress and work, such "hothouse" creatures could not long survive in the far from cordial environment of the world beyond the laboratory.

Since the electrical impulses of an inhibitory message are no different from those of an excitatory message, there arises the question of how these impersonal impulses can produce such dramatically opposite results. Although the story is still incomplete, we know that throughout the entire nervous system the critical agents of translation and transmission are minute amounts of specific chemicals released at the synaptic junctions between neurons as well as between the neuron and its final effector organ. In the autonomic nervous system acetylcholine and certain members of the adrenaline family are the more important chemical messengers.

Control Centers

The autonomic nervous system is a somewhat untidy and independent division, sufficiently original in its connections and duties so that it must be separately classified and studied. Perhaps because it functions underground and is concerned with processes we do not ordinarily control, we tend—as long as it is in good working order—to take it for granted. Anatomically it seems to have made a dash for freedom, and yet we must now ask how automatic, how "autonomous," is our involuntary nervous system?

Certainly it is not as independent as was once believed. The autonomic nervous system has central offices in the lower parts of the brain as well as centers recently discovered in the cerebral cortex itself. It is influenced from above by thought and emotion and is itself an important instrument for the expression of emotion. It becomes more and more apparent that this industrious, dependable division has not entirely escaped the domination of the highest level of the brain; it has merely been let out on a loose rein.

When we move away from valuable but isolated textbook diagrams to take a more realistic view of the living, working body, it becomes obvious that the buried autonomic nervous system must work intimately with its companion, the voluntary system, from which it borrows its routes from the outside world. The sensory arm of many autonomic reflexes originates in the external sense organs and runs to autonomic headquarters along the sensory paths of the voluntary nervous system. A sudden loud noise, originally perceived by the ear and delivered to the brain, may cause the heart to beat faster and the blood pressure to jump. The aroma of a fresh apple pie baking in the oven, traveling in electrical form from the nostrils to the brain, may cause you to salivate. The mere picture of a juicy apple pie in a magazine or nothing more than its mental image may trigger impulses in a parasympathetic nerve which in turn will stimulate the salivary glands to perform just as they would for a real apple pie.

Although usually we do not control the functioning of our internal machinery, such conscious control is not necessarily impossible; more likely its achievement is impractical for most of us. After long years of practice, members of various Eastern cults as well as physiologists experimenting on themselves have learned to perform the most curious and bizarre feats. They are able to erect the hair on their arms, prevent bleeding from an open wound, and regulate their heart beat, breathing, metabolism, and digestive processes. The most distinguished performers of this grotesque art can tune down their vital processes until a state quite like hibernation is reached. In this condition of minimal life they may be buried alive and yet after a considerable period of time emerge alive and unharmed. The Indian fakir who, by mental effort, has tamed his reactions to pain, who walks and reclines on a bed of nails, and who can alter the rhythm of his heartbeat, earns his simple living by the unique method of controlling his reflexes. It would seem that even in the so-called involuntary nervous system, where there is sufficient will, there may be a way.

Unfortunately there are times when influences from higher centers become a nuisance and interfere with the normal activity of our internal organs. Worry and excitement may upset the digestive machinery so that it no longer functions smoothly. More often than not, nausea, vomiting, constipation, and diarrhea are the replies of the digestive tract to meddling emotions. Occasionally, if it is even suggested that the egg you have just swallowed may be rotten or that the milk may be curdled, the direction of traffic in the alimentary canal may be dramatically reversed.

Physicians are familiar with the intimate but often unwholesome relationship between the mind and the tissues of the body. The much misunderstood field of psychosomatic medicine is concerned not with imaginary ills but with real diseases and disorders of bodily structures and functions for which emotions are responsible. It is not magic which accounts for psychosomatic disturbances but rather the intimate, although admittedly puzzling, connections between higher centers in the brain and our internal organs and glands. Why, under stress, one brain helps to gouge an ulcer in the stomach and another does not is a mystery both psychologists and physiologists are working hard to solve.

The actual paths of autonomic fibers traveling through the spinal cord are not too well known. The more important autonomic control centers are found in the medulla, the midbrain, the cerebellum, the hypothalamus, and in the smell brain and the frontal lobes of the cerebrum.

The tiny hypothalamus, which is connected by important nerve routes to the cerebral cortex and to the chairman of the endocrine system, the pituitary gland, is now recognized as the great switching and coordinating station for the autonomic nervous system. With connections so intricate that they probably weave through all levels of the brain, the hypothalamus is well equipped for the task of regulating our internal structures so that they serve the coordinated needs of the entire organism—an organism which may be suspended in the twilight world of sleep or taking an examination or running a four-minute mile. By day and by night the hypothalamus remains the guardian of our internal environment and ultimately the overseer of a hidden physicochemical kingdom.

If we are at all inclined to regard the autonomic nervous system as a necessary but dull department of our neural equipment, we must remember that it is this system which contributes heavily to the production of emotional reactions. How did this evolve? The hypothalamus is intimately concerned with the nourishment and reproduction of the body. In lower animals the sense of smell plays an extremely important role in obtaining food, avoiding enemies, and in directing the sexual drives which assure the future of the species. In these animals a close relationship exists between the hypothalamus, the executive smell brain, and the nerves which carry messages to and from the organs of the body. Long ago a brain went hunting for dinner and a mate and established for all time the nerve patterns which linked basic drives to visceral affairs.

The human smell brain has outgrown much of its early usefulness. Nevertheless it still retains its original affiliation with the autonomic nervous system and with those fundamental reactions by which a human being displays emotion. Above the humble smell brain blossomed the massive, versatile cerebral hemispheres, which took over and elaborated the executive duties once modestly carried out by the smell brain. The increased participation of the raveled lobes of the cerebrum in the regulation of our internal machinery and the frequent subjugation of this supposedly autonomic system to its extremely subtle and intricate master have certainly made our involuntary nervous system more fascinating but unfortunately more vulnerable.

7

THE ENIGMA OF EMOTION

The paths of emotion wind through so many levels of human activity that the trail is difficult to follow. Eventually all footprints vanish and emotion itself— private, invisible, and known intimately only to its owner—floats somewhere beyond its pursuer's reach. What, we may ask, is anger? Is it a hand raised in wrath, a contraction of skeletal muscles, a warm flush, or a racing heart? Is it an unpleasantly flavored thought or perhaps the flavor without the thought? Is anger to be regarded merely as the heightened activity of neurons clustered in a displeasure center in the brain? Probably anger is all of these, since our emotions are complex, elusive phenomena intimately entwined with many other processes, some as fundamental as breathing, others as personal as perception or as complex as thinking. Often it is impossible to pry an emotion loose from the other activities it colors and enriches and by which it is, in turn, influenced.

From Electricity to Experience

As the course of this book turns toward the higher processes of the human brain, we enter a realm in which we know "less and less about more and more." Admittedly, the history of science is filled with memorable instances in which yesterday's proven facts have been replaced by what is considered "proven" today. When we explore the mental forests of our brain, we enter a region where even facts are few, where theories sprout abundant as weeds, and where, if we are not to lose our way, we must take care to distinguish between what we know and what we only assume.

There is no reason for us to shrink from this fascinating subject—one which contains the secrets of why I am I, why you are you, and why we recognize the distinction—but we must proceed with caution and cool heads. The most satisfactory data concerning emotions as well as other mental processes have been obtained from animal experiments, and the gap which separates the animal brain from the human brain is one in which many an impressive theory has foundered. We can study the cat's brain and project our discoveries onto its human counterpart, but enthusiasm must be tempered with restraint, for many functions served by lower levels of the animal's brain have moved upstairs in the human brain, and the two organs are not directly comparable.

Today most people agree that mental function in some way results from the activity of our brain cells, for without the brain, emotion, thought, memory, and imagination are inconceivable. However, the innocent little words "in some way" glide smoothly over a problem so perplexing that many a stout-hearted scientist has expressed the fear that it may be insoluble. Despite all that we know about the brain, despite our ability to trace the path of the nerve impulse which causes a hand to move, we still do not know how electrical impulses are converted into feelings, thoughts, ideas, into the special flavor and identity of a memory, and for that matter even into the images we see.

The well-studied visual process serves as a simple illustration of this ultimate obstacle in relating the brain to the experiences it projects. When we look at a tree standing on a hillside, its image travels to the sensitive retina in the back of each eye. Because of our peculiar optical system, the images are received upside down. From the retina these impulses are relayed as a common electrical commodity to the visual center in the cerebral cortex, where an event takes place for which we still have no explanation: We see. First the brain reinverts the topsy-turvy images. Then an electrochemical disturbance occurring within the brain and beneath the vault of bone is mysteriously projected beyond the surfaces of the brain and the body to a point in space where it is perceived and recognized as a tree. Scientists have yet to bridge the gap between electricity and the final event in the chain—personal experience; between electrical patterns in the brain and the sight of trees on a hillside or the color, tone, and content of our emotions and ideas.

Asset or Liability

Our emotional machinery is sensitive, subtle, and so complicated that it now operates in a world of symbols that only vaguely represent needs which were once obviously biological. In its more primitive form in both man and animal, emotion summons the individual to satisfy basic needs—such as hunger, sexual activity, comfort, and safety—and supplies the drive required for this pursuit. In animals the relationship between the basic need and the emotion it generates is usually quite simple. Withhold food from a hungry dog and he is soon both hungry and angry. Because our brain is more sophisticated than the dog's, our problems are proportionately more complex.

Human beings need not be hungry to display an emotion which is nevertheless indirectly concerned with food. For example, in the midst of plenty we may "worry" about next month's food supply. What is more, this anxiety may take the form of concern for the job which provides the money which assures, among other things, a contented stomach. Similarly, in the human being the mechanism of this system need not be triggered by the actual scent of friend or foe. It can be set off by a symbol such as an insult or complaint.

As a driving force emotion is immensely potent and —as long as it is effectively controlled—valuable. Without emotion muscles would produce movement, memories would settle, and thoughts might still pursue each other around the circuits of the brain. However, deprived of the focusing power of emotion these processes would be no more than disorganized, ineffective fragments of behavior, and human performance would limp along without purpose or direction. Emotion is indeed a priceless force. Miraculous feats of strength have been performed by people whose physiological energies have been mobilized by fear. Ambition is only one of many emotions which keep students at their books. And in the name of love, garden walls have been scaled, great poetry has been written, and everywhere men and women concentrate their energies on the demanding task of creating a home and raising their children. Unfortunately when emotion escapes from control and overflows its banks, its greatest virtue becomes a defect: The force of unrestrained hatred may blind a person to his own safety and best interests, love cannot long afford to be blind, and worry may so usurp a mind that it can no longer attend effectively to its duties.

Emotion in the Laboratory

Translated literally, the word "emotion" means "moving out." Actually emotion has two faces. We use the word to mean both emotional expression and an inward state. Therefore we must distinguish between the way an angry person expresses his emotions and the inner, subjective feelings themselves; between the way it looks and the way it feels. Emotional reaction has been the subject of much careful study. However, the problem of measuring and evaluating the subjective experience—the "feeling" of grief or joy, of love or hate—presents enormous experimental obstacles. By its very nature elusive and personal, emotional experience does not lend itself to laboratory study.

It is not difficult to understand why this is so. Although we may study the behavior of frightened or angry animals, they cannot tell us what they feel. The fact that human beings possess the gift of speech and are able to communicate their feelings by no means solves the problem. How do you describe joy, guilt, or even so crude a feeling as pain so that you are certain that another person, one with quite a different set of attitudes and values, understands exactly what it is you have experienced? We can devise experiments in which we measure the intensity of a given pain stimulus and the level at which different subjects react to it. But what a sharp needle feels like—the "feel" of feeling—may be described in a doctor's office or in a book of poetry, but it cannot be objectively measured. Despite our rich language, we often fail to communicate our feelings accurately. When a student is asked how his English examination was and groans, "Terrible!" a correct translation might be, "Could have been worse!"

Emotional responses are easier to study, and yet

they also may be misleading unless we consider both the circumstances and the individual in which they appear. A spitting, clawing cat, with dilated pupils and bristling hair, may be an angry cat—or a frightened cat; and occasionally human beings decline to laugh with joy but weep instead. Because a person does not display his emotions, it does not mean that he lacks feelings; nor is the intensity of a response a satisfactory gauge of the depth of emotional feeling. The stoic Eskimo or the calm, well-controlled individual may feel deeply and yet appear outwardly unmoved. On the other hand a "high-strung" or uninhibited person may, with little provocation, be catapulted into a weeping, handwringing performance which is not an accurate indication of the feelings it appears to represent. Even within the same individual the readiness of emotion to perform and the style it chooses may vary from day to day, influenced by such factors as illness, fatigue, and shifting degrees of interest.

We are quite free to study the emotional behavior of animals, but controlled studies of emotional reactions in human beings are difficult to carry out because of the problem of reproducing these responses in the artificial atmosphere of the laboratory. Scientists cannot be blamed for their reluctance to sacrifice friendships and good will for juicy exhibitions of emotion. What is more, even the most stinging insult may no longer produce an angry reaction if the subject knows it was dealt to him as part of an experiment.

What is pleasure to one person may not be to another or, like the insult, may fail entirely in the laboratory world of synthetic experience.

Not only are our emotions experimentally unwieldy, they are also difficult to classify. We do not know how many patterns or combinations of emotion there are in human beings. Emotions are commonly separated into two main categories: pleasant and unpleasant. In animal studies it is convenient, certainly, to recognize three basic emotional responses: fear, anger, and pleasure. In man, however, between these extremes there lies a vast palette of feeling and response: Joy, sorrow, shame, surprise, love, anxiety, and contentment are but a few of emotion's many brilliant and subtle shades.

What part of our emotional behavior is inborn and what part is the product of individual experience and social pressure is still undetermined. How ancient are our feelings? Is man born with an instinct to fight? Does he inherit his fears, loves, and hates? We do not know. Many feel the answer may involve a combination of inherited and acquired factors. Studies of human infants, which ought to reveal man in his most primitive condition at a time when he is closest to his basic genetic inheritance, are hindered by the fact that the adult cannot remember the first months of his life. The subject of all the fuss is equally uncooperative, for as yet he cannot tell us what he really feels when he wrinkles his face in what appears to be a smile, or cries with what his mother—or the scientist bending over him—concludes must be anger, fear, or perhaps pain.

It is not surprising, therefore, that the vital, explosive subject of emotion has caused many a scientist to leap into the fray, frequently with his own emotions flying high. For years men have wrestled with the thorny problem of explaining the relationship between emotional behavior and emotional experience. Do we feel first and then react? Or is the emotional reaction itself the source of our feelings?

Toward the end of the nineteenth century the eminent philosopher and psychologist William James was one of those who stated that our feelings are not aroused primarily in consciousness but result from the physical reactions of the body. For example, we are afraid because our heart beats faster, our blood vessels constrict, and our skeletal muscles contract in preparation for flight. Said James, "We are afraid because we run; we do not run because we are afraid."

As physiologists learned more about the nervous system, they tested this hypothesis by removing the sympathetic system of cats, in this way eliminating the automatic responses commonly involved in reactions of fear and fright. When provoked, these experimental cats hissed and clawed like angry cats; they could still act emotionally. William James was wrong, the experimenters concluded. We are first afraid and then our heart beats faster.

Today many observers believe that both of these

classic theories have oversimplified a matter which was never simple in the first place. William James was not entirely wrong, for we all know that a throbbing heart and a stomach "tied up in knots" do indeed contribute to the experience of fright and may actually aggravate our uncomfortable feeling. On the other hand, deep feeling is possible even though a person neither blanches nor trembles. Certainly it would be a mistake to interpret the instrument recording of an astronaut's well-disciplined internal machinery as either the true measure or the source of the deep emotion he must experience as he looks down upon our planet while orbiting through space.

The Body Performs

The vast dramatic repertoire of emotion is an actor's delight. Yet its command performances as well as its involuntary displays may easily be divided into two groups: First, we recognize the familiar responses produced by our skeletal muscles. Although we do not have a tail to wag, we indicate our feelings by a wide range of facial expressions, by gesture and sound, and by changes in posture. We cry, laugh, frown, and smile; we cringe or run with fear, jump with fright, clap our hands and dance with joy. We have already noted that as a measure of emotion these responses of our voluntary nervous system, although dramatic and accessible, are unreliable.

The *involuntary* responses of our internal organs,

under the control of the autonomic nervous system and the endocrine glands, tell the rest of emotion's story and are, on the whole, a more accurate gauge of emotional events. The sweaty palms and dry mouth of stage fright are familiar to many of us. We all have felt our heartbeat quicken with excitement or upon awakening suddenly from a bad dream, have experienced the deliberate pounding of a heart flooded with fear. Because these bodily reactions are often so striking, it is understandable that when at last the brain began to be linked with sensation, movement, and thought, the seats of deep feeling and passion were still relegated by men of considerable competence to outlying regions of the body. Relics of this enduring error are sprinkled through our daily language. Those of us who are brave possess "guts," "stout hearts," and "backbones," while "faint hearts," "cold feet," and "yellow streaks" distinguish the cowardly.

The lie detector is a device designed to take advantage of our inability to control the intimate revelations of our involuntary nervous system. This instrument supposedly registers the flare of guilt and fear which occurs when we do not tell the truth. Modern lie detectors record combinations of respiration and pulse rate, blood pressure and the electrical conductivity of the skin. But the machine is as fallible as emotion is fickle. In police proceedings the evidence obtained in this way must be carefully evaluated and cannot always be admitted to the courtroom. The lie detector is helpless when confronted with a person who cannot tell right from wrong or who honestly believes he has acted properly. What is more, anger, nervousness, or even feelings of guilt not directly related to the lie in question may confuse the emotional picture so that the lie detector lies. Frequently the instrument is most effective as a psychological weapon. The criminal who fears he is about to have his mind read by an all-knowing tangle of wires and electrodes may break down and confess his crime.

Highways of the Mind

Up to this point we have pictured nerve circuits as sensorimotor arcs which swiftly link input with output: Foot follows foot, lungs billow and deflate, and all creatures from starfish to scientists presumably withdraw from danger. And yet we know that neither people nor nerve circuits are this simple. At times the scientist risks radioactive exposure, the soldier holds on to an ignited grenade, and the housewife tries not to drop a hot dish on the floor. Before we pursue emotion into its cerebral lodgings, it will be helpful to glance briefly at the sweeping, tangled patterns of nerve traffic within the brain itself. Sometimes fleeting, often enduring, always magnificent, these are the endless journeys of comparison, innovation, of check and countercheck which make the human brain the most intricate, subtle, and creative instrument on earth.

The neural highways of the mind must be at least as

complicated as the experiences they represent, and neither emotion nor any other mental state can claim exclusive rights to precious brain territory or be expected to travel a private path. It has been estimated that millions of neurons are involved in the recall of a single memory. Despite our wealth of brain cells we would quickly run out of equipment were it not that the versatile, hard-working neuron has many responsibilities and participates in multiple patterns of behavior. The number of possible interconnections among the cells of the brain is beyond all imagination.

Let us return to the useful example of vision. If vision were limited to the eye, the optic nerve, and the small area of visual cortex, then the image of a tree, of the print on this page, or of your friend Tom would make a useless trip to the brain and be projected as a meaningless blob of light and color. For Tom to be Tom, the sensory information sent to the visual cortex must circulate to other parts of the brain, so that you are aware that you have seen "something," so that the "something" is perceived in the shape of a human being and recognized specifically as Tom. The experience may now fire a battery of other responses; old memories are pried loose, emotions and thoughts speed along other channels of the brain, and finally Tom goes into storage. There he may be held in the superficial or deep archives of memory for hours, weeks, or years until the key which fits the lock is turned and the image of the Tom who appeared here today emerges, undeniably Tom, but subtly altered by the mysterious whims of the storage process.

The amount of brain traffic which accounts for the phenomenon of "Tom" must be tremendous. To risk a mechanical analogy, the brain resembles a computer rather than a telephone switchboard with the simple duty of rewarding calls with appropriate answers. The concept of one neuron tapping another on the shoulder and forwarding an impulse is oversimplified. It is estimated that each neuron in the brain receives connections from 100 other neurons and in turn communicates with 100 more. A stimulus traveling along a single neuron may activate 100,000 neurons in one second. The wave front of impulses which now advance through the cortex is less like a sleek, pointed arrow speeding toward a single destination than like a mighty wave, advancing in a great crescendo. Within the wave, streams of traffic, moving at different speeds, continually converge and diverge. Part of this flow may depart from the main stream, perhaps to cross a bridge to the other cerebral hemisphere or to loop downward into lower centers before returning to the main force of the advancing front.

Frequently waves of impulses continue to circulate over an established route long after the original stimulus is gone. Physiologists call such closed, self-excitatory loops *reverberating circuits*, and here indeed may be

Fig. 22 *Schematic drawing of a reverberating circuit in left cerebral hemisphere*

the circuitry of tension, anxiety, dreams, and unsolved problems (see Fig. 22). Around and around the circuit impulses pursue each other, carrying on the unresolved business of the brain, sometimes dying out, sometimes "breaking in" the synaptic connections and reinforcing the pattern, as when a habit is set or a memory established. From the original stream, impulses may flow into other channels. Memory summons memory, and in the same way that insight or the solution to a problem seems to dart from older, unsatisfactory paths, impulses may depart entirely from traditional routes and venture into new brain territory. Although we do not know, it is easy to imagine that the lively, creative mind may be the one in which many new channels are constantly opened, in which channels communicate easily with each other, and in which stereotyped, automatic routes are not allowed to suffice for all the brain's work.

If we imagine the complexity and grandeur of many such traffic fronts in the brain—each advancing, dying out, converging, separating, and each shifting within its own lanes—it may be easier to understand why our rich, complex mental life is woven of so many different strands; why it is difficult to separate emotion from thought, learning from memory, even love from hate.

Cerebral Lodgings

The drama of emotion unfolds both on stage and behind the scenes in the interior of the body. At this point the question arises: How does the brain produce and direct the emotional performance? Later we shall ask where emotion is felt. Man owes his most glorious accomplishments as much to emotion as to its dry companion intellect. The key to the origin and control of emotion—if we could find it—would be a valuable prize, for, diffuse and potent, emotion knows how to destroy as well as create.

The cerebral offices of emotion are still inadequately explored, although current studies have provided important new pieces in the puzzle. It appears that the centers which produce emotional behavior are located at all levels of the brain, from its cortex to its stem. Emotion and its antecedents in lower animals have been with the brain for a very long time. The basic centers of emotional behavior follow a central axis, almost through the core of the organ, running down the cerebrum along the groove which divides the two hemispheres. They spread into the smell brain on its floor, to the thalamus and hypothalamus, and finally extend into the primitive brain stem.

From animal experiments and from studies of human disease we know that various autonomic emotional reactions, such as changes in blood pressure and breathing, have "ground floor" offices in the brain stem. In the case of the more vivid emotions, such as anger and fear, it appears that the hypothalamus, with its sensitive devices for regulating the vast concert of body rhythms, is responsible for organizing these fragments of emotional behavior into a well-coordinated although incomplete emotional performance. This tiny station is actually a powerful plant, capable of manufacturing a somewhat crude emotional product. It must still send elsewhere for certain missing parts, such as postural responses. Above all, the meaning, distribution, and control of its product must be supplied by higher management in the cerebral cortex.

Depending upon the part of the cortex removed, experimental animals can be made excessively ferocious or unusually placid. Thus without its smell brain the hypothalamus of the dog and cat produces not true rage but *sham rage*. Such animals are extremely touchy and easily angered, indicating that it is the ancient part of an animal's cortex, the smell brain, which normally keeps its more violent emotions in check. The cortex, however, does more than inhibit; it gives meaning and direction to emotion. Deprived of its perceptual and spatial senses, of its memory files and its power to "put two and two together," an animal lacking a cerebral cortex will snap aimlessly through the air, unable to locate the hand which has touched its tail. Lacking the brain to bear a grudge, its anger dissolves as soon as the annoyance ceases. There is more to true anger than bark and bite, and sham rage is an impostor—ineffective, futile, and meaningless.

Demonstrations of the loss of cortical control in human beings are harder to arrange, and yet frequently people about to receive general anesthesia blush at the thought of the "awful things" they might say and do if, even temporarily, the restraining influence of the cortex were lifted. For it is quite true that patients in the first stages of anesthesia often thrash about, groan, laugh, and rave before unconsciousness mercifully drops its curtain on the primitive brain's brief fling in the center of the stage.

Where Feeling Dwells

Normally we are not at the mercy of our raw emotions. Anger is curbed, the soldier masters his fear and goes off to battle, and we distinguish among pleasures, pursuing some and denying others. This complicated type of control resides in the cortex. We know little—

and even that is confusing—about the anatomy and physiology of its mechanism. In fact we are uncertain of where our wily emotions themselves are lodged.

Scientists who have had considerable success in locating the centers of emotional expression have found the search for the seat of feeling more baffling. Curious to know what happens to our nerve cells when they are angry or "fall in love," physiologists have probed the brains of animals, seeking specific structures or their combinations in which emotions, such as anger, fear, and pleasure, may be said to dwell. The ancient thalamus is known to be the region in which the sensation of pain first becomes conscious, and it is here, in what some have called the "factory of feeling," that many of our higher feelings, as well, are probably crudely experienced. It appears that it is the thalamus which is the "animal in us," for only as the cortex develops from lower animals to higher, from infant to adult, is the power of the exuberant thalamus curbed.

Tentative conclusions based on animal experiments suggest that actual seats of emotion exist, that certain parts of the brain do indeed house our basic drives. According to this concept the brain is more than an alarm system and coordinating center; it is itself a sensory organ in which specific areas are tuned to the still unknown processes which account for our basic drives. Just as an appropriately stimulated receptor in the eye initiates a response called "seeing," the brain itself may contain the receptors for the chemical and electrical occurrences which produce our feelings. We all know that if they "care to," the highest levels of our brain can control our drives and appetites. But what are motivation and ambition? What is that mysterious force called will power? There is now some evidence, obtained from studies of hunger and appetite, which suggests that motivation is not some misty vapor, but that its mechanism may actually be built into the cell structure of the brain.

Scientists exploring this problem have already discovered specific areas of the rat's hypothalamus which control appetite. By introducing appropriate chemicals directly into this appetite center, they have found it possible to manipulate the rat's appetite. This is a discovery which should bring cheer, if not relief, to those of us who must continue to tackle our appetite centers with will power as our sole weapon. At the same time, these scientists seem to have located a distinct pleasure center within the rat's tiny brain, for there are reports of hungry animals which actually prefer a suitably directed electrical stimulus to satisfaction by the "old-fashioned" means of food. Their hunger is thus satisfied, at least temporarily, in the brain instead of the stomach. We do not have to look far to find human beings whose appetites are dissolved by the anticipation of an examination or an interview, by engrossing work or falling in love. The physiology of hunger covers a vast territory, including every living cell in the body. In the rat, scientists have at last tapped the cerebral end of this circuitry. It is a promising discovery, for it should eventually lead to an understanding of the cerebral processes by which appetite is driven beyond the physiological demands represented by hunger and by which the thresholds of our other drives and "appetites" are altered.

The ultimate value of this kind of research, however, is not to take the struggle out of dieting or to provide us with a set of pill-controlled "instant emotions." If we are to discover what happens to a brain in mental disease, it is essential that we understand how a healthy brain functions: We must learn the source of its drives, the mechanism of motivation, and the techniques by which it handles frustration and stress. Brain tumors, diseases of brain tissue, and metabolic deficiencies affecting brain cells are common enough, but frequently the disease process appears to be invisible. On the one hand, we observe signs and symptoms often appearing in the form of strange or inappropriate behavior. On the other hand, the psychiatrist points not to a tumor but to specific disturbing experiences in the life of the individual which have triggered the illness. Between these experiences and the observable symptoms of illness, however, the road vanishes from sight.

And so there is a tendency to cover our uncomfortable ignorance of the fundamental mechanisms of mental disease by refusing to admit that it is "real." We do not really know why certain patterns continue to reverberate through a brain, why emotional equations sometimes are never balanced, or what happens to brain cells when certain powerful needs are denied satisfaction. What has occurred within the badly behaving brain, the nature of its specific deficiency, or perhaps excess, and the ultimate mechanisms which disrupts the smooth functioning of an apparently healthy organ continue to elude us. Were we to find the answer, we might not only help the mentally ill but preserve the mental health of millions of other human beings.

8

TUNING YOU IN

The origins of consciousness are veiled in the past. Its mechanisms are still unknown, and even its definition is controversial. Yet the triumph of consciousness in the human brain is so magnificent that every human being senses dimly but accurately that consciousness or awareness is his most precious gift. As part of the highest integrating processes of the brain it is the human form of consciousness which sets man apart from beast and from which issues the full glory of human achievement.

The subject of consciousness is immense and perplexing and our understanding of its physiology pitfully inadequate. The word itself is confusing. Philosopher, writer, psychologist, and psychiatrist have endowed this accommodating term with a vast assortment of meaning. In the physiological sense alone, the varieties of consciousness are so many and subtle that William James spoke perceptively when he said that everyone knows what consciousness is until he attempts to define it. In one sense the problem of consciousness is not a matter of whether an individual is conscious or not but of *how* conscious he is. "There is no such entity as consciousness—in health we are from moment to moment differently conscious," observed a famous neurologist who, like others, regarded consciousness not as a condition, any more than breathing is a condition, but as a state—the process of awareness. Consciousness therefore may be described in the physiological sense as an *organism's awareness of itself and its relationship to its environment.*

The Evolution of Consciousness

If this is what we mean by consciousness, it is then but a quick step to the most fascinating of all the questions raised by this perplexing subject: Who is a conscious creature? Shall we grant consciousness to the human infant lying helpless yet impressionable in his crib, his precocious brain still unfinished, his nervous system not yet wired? Do apes know who they are? How many cages away do their horizons extend? Is the dog aware of himself and the world in which he lives, and if so, what is that awareness like? As we gaze through the water at a fish circling a worm on the end of a hook, darting back and forth, hesitating, timing its movements before striking, we realize that the fish lacks the words to ask: Shall I? Shall I not? Yet we cannot help wondering what may be the form of awareness—of hesitation and then decision—in this lowly animal. As we move down the animal scale into the vast invertebrate world, our curiosity is perhaps tinged with pity, for intuitively we suspect that the subtlety and richness of awareness decline as animals become simpler. Without benefit of further reading or formal study, each of us already senses a basic truth about consciousness—that it is not the private possession of man, that animals claim it in differing degrees of complexity, and that, for all this, human consciousness remains privileged and unique.

Although we cannot determine the starting point in the evolution of consciousness, its origins must be very old. Most authorities agree that even the lowest animals have some form of primitive awareness in proportion to the development of their brains. It is a matter of debate whether it can be said that the various one-celled animals drifting in the primeval slime were even dimly conscious. Throughout invertebrate history the growth of consciousness probably paralleled the search for food and the extent to which this pursuit was a voluntary function. As the humble crab poses and solves the mealtime problem—if I go now and in this direction, I shall dine; in another direction or at another time, I shall be dinner—it is probably aware of its relationship to its environment both in space and in time. In considering the consequences of its conduct the crab exercises choice and is therefore at least crudely conscious. Despite their complex social behavior insects, by these standards, may be less conscious creatures, for their elaborate behavior is frozen in fixed, automatic reflexes, and their seeming vitality is not original but is dictated by an inherited master pattern which winds and runs all the individuals of a species.

About 300 million years ago certain ancient vertebrate fish found themselves stifling in the stagnant, shallow waters created by the harsh climate of the Devonian period and rose to the surface to gulp air. In time, these first air-breathing fish developed true lungs and sturdy stumps where once fins had been. Abandoning their shrinking, watery world, they flopped out onto the land, there to try their luck. On this new, exotic terrain the other great vertebrate orders evolved. As the problems of finding food, providing safety, and protecting the young grew more complex, and as muscle, nerve, and brain responded to the challenge, so too, we may assume, did consciousness grow.

Yet we have no way of knowing what this primitive awareness was like. It is difficult enough for human beings, possessing the gift of speech, to communicate the essence of individual experience to each other. The nature of an animal's conscious experience may be inferred, but it cannot really be determined. Not only does the animal lack the necessary language but its sense organs do not always parallel our own. To the extent that they are different they reproduce a world we can imagine but never know. The sharp-eyed vulture coasting effortlessly through the skies can spot carrion lying on the ground several miles away. The dog's world is blurred and colorless but pungent with smells and vivid with sounds lost to the human sensory apparatus. Many fish are equipped with special distance receptors distributed through their skin. Acutely sensitive to vibration, they help the fish locate enemies and prey with uncanny skill. What is it like to have such "feeling" skin? We can only guess. Moreover, just as we are unaware of the sensory organs which help us maintain balance—buried in our muscles and joints and in the inner ear—so we have no way of knowing whether the fish has conscious experience of its own remarkable distance receptors.

It is almost impossible for us to imagine the flavor and quality of primitive consciousness, for we who are human and who therefore cherish what has been called our *I-ness* or *Me-ness* cannot easily conceive of levels of consciousness which do not include an awareness of the "self" as a distinct and separate entity. Yet awareness of ourselves as individual beings is only one of the more elaborate forms of consciousness, dependent on rich memory stores, the complex circuitry of our association tracts, and a highly-developed time sense.

The fully conscious individual, whether man or crab, is aware of his orientation not only in space but in time as well. There are, it is true, organic disturbances of the nervous system in which this orientation is lost. The afflicted person remains alert and responsive and is competent to make judgments other than those involving orientation either in space or in time. To be fully conscious, however, even the most primitive animal must be able to link one moment with the next at least long enough to anticipate the immediate future and make decisions vital to survival and safety. In lower animals and newborn infants this primitive kind of consciousness may consist of nothing more than brief flashes of awareness. As the cortex evolves in higher animals and as it develops in the growing child, cortical memory is added to crude awareness, linking these separate flashes of consciousness so that past and present are fused, giving experience the seeming continuity of a running camera film. The rules which determine the way in which the individual "frames" of consciousness succeed each other remain a mystery, but in some way it is the unique cortical memory of the human being which binds and preserves the myriad fragments of individual experience, finally creating the illusion of that continuous "self" of which each of us is intimately and acutely aware.

At some time in our lives most of us, sorrowing for a dead pet, have paused to wonder what the animal "felt," for it is natural to measure another creature's feelings in terms of our own. No one can be certain, but granting that the animal may have been frightened, that it struggled and wanted to live, we may take comfort in the knowledge that its experience must have been different from ours. An animal cannot regard its life or regret its loss in quite the way we do, for to our knowledge it has never been able to think about its own life as something separate and special. It has never examined itself as a creature living in a given amount of time, for whom there was birth and will be death, and beyond whose brief life span there was a past and there will be a future. According to our definition we cannot deny consciousness to animals. The ape knows well enough what it is doing, and if it was significant, remembers what it once did. Nor should we exclude the infant simply because it has not yet discovered its self as something apart from all the rest of the world. Because lack of communication prevents us from probing the conscious experience of other creatures, we are treading on brittle ground when we arbitrarily state that animals lack self-knowledge. However, from what we observe it does appear that adult man is different from all other creatures. He alone has the power to stand apart and reflect upon himself: Only the human being is aware of his awareness; only man *knows* that he knows.

We do not know where, in what forgotten time, and among what manner of early creatures who stood between ape and man, the dawn of human consciousness occurred. The first step in the direction of man was taken when some halfway creature looked in upon himself and discovered: I am I—someone distinct and separate from the rest of creation.

The ability to "know ourselves" was probably a gift of the association tracts in the great frontal lobes which most distinguish the human brain from the ape brain. When, for example, the nerve tracts leading to these lobes are severed to relieve unbearable pain, the patient ceases to suffer because he regards the pain impersonally, as if it existed outside of his body. At the same time, although intelligence is hardly impaired, such patients become somewhat silly and uninhibited, having lost those qualities which are particularly human—ambition, initiative, judgment, and foresight. If his frontal lobes are disconnected, man may be freed from suffering, but he sacrifices his ability to move about in time, to plan for the future, to form ethical and moral judgments, and to evolve the values which are part of our civilization. In the frontal lobes, to a great extent, dwell our essential humanity and—paradoxically—our inhumanity.

Once he had discovered himself, man was free to discover others, to project himself into the life of another individual, to imagine another person's emotions and thoughts, and even, as we have just done, to speculate upon the nature of animal experience. To I-ness was added You-ness. Tentatively, persistently, and then as now, imperfectly, he began to spin forth the bridges, not of physical need and contact but of understanding. "No man is an island, entire of itself," because a web of consciousness links him not only with his fellow man but with all the creatures of the earth. It is a unique and precious gift which bears with it the grave responsibility to behave in the best of human, not animal, tradition.

Brain Waves

During the course of the day consciousness waxes and wanes, fluctuating from the extremes of drowsiness and sleep through that semiattentive state in which, quite remarkably, we conduct most of our daily affairs, to alert states in which we are excited, vigilant, or in which awareness is narrowed to permit intense concentration. The content of consciousness is equally variable. Hallucinations and illusions may warp its countenance; in the form of dreams which weave their luminous trails through the dark fabric of the sleeper's night, consciousness is fragmentary and often distorted.

Consciousness is suspended in deep sleep, in coma, and during deep anesthesia. But unlike the comatose or the anesthetized person, who is lost to the call of the outer world and to internal signals, the sleeper can be aroused by an appropriate stimulus: a hand on his shoulder, the sound of his name, the call of infant or alarm clock.

Alterations in our states of consciousness are vividly illustrated by the electrical handwriting of our brain cells, reproduced in the electroencephalogram. In interpretating these complex "brain prints," however, many a scientist has found himself more than a little lost among the EEG waves. As we become drowsy and relax, gradually sinking into oblivion, the continuous, regular waves, the ripples of wakefulness appearing on the recording paper, are replaced by the slow, giant rhythms of sleep, which seem to blot out all other kinds of activity. It is interesting that the billowy "handwriting" of sleep is also the signature of certain kinds of brain disease as well as being the dominant and normal pattern during the first year of life.

On the other hand, the electrical rhythms of hypnosis do not resemble those of sleep. It has been suggested that far from being asleep, the hypnotized person is in a state of increased awareness in which, however, the hypnotist has taken over the task of feeding the external sensory input into the circuits of his subject's brain and has reordered the mechanisms of consciousness in such a way that he can manipulate the manner in which the sensory input is handled in the brain.

Diseases or injuries may affect consciousness by disorganizing the normal electrical patterns of the brain in a manner which is frequently characteristic. During an epileptic seizure the orderly discharging of brain cells, which like good soldiers normally troop together in battalions, is interrupted by a few sick cells which suddenly go wild and discharge chaotically. The electrical storm starts in a limited area but rapidly spreads to other cortical areas, sending panic through the ranks of previously well-behaved cells. Depending upon the areas affected, the disrupted cells now produce the frenzied activity, the convulsions, the strange sensory disturbances, and the loss of consciousness found in different degrees in the many forms of epilepsy. Similarly, it is believed that a severe blow to the head produces unconsciousness by stampeding the orderly pattern of pulsing brain cells with a chaotic discharge of electrical activity.

Turning Us On

It is futile to explore the brain, searching for a single seat of consciousness. Subtle and multiform, the entire body its domain, consciousness is created by the integration of many complex neural states. Consciousness begins—and ends—with the contribution of the sensory system. The continuous stream of sensory impulses which pour into the brain from all parts of the body creates the content of conscious experience. At the same time, this sensory input is also the source of the energy which keeps the nervous system awake. The human nervous system has been compared to a radio which cannot receive signals until it is turned on, and so too must we be "turned on," or conscious, before we can be aware of sensory stimuli.

Thus consciousness alters as the contribution of the various senses is diminished or reorganized. When we are tired the threshold of sensory reception is suppressed. When occasionally we go "wool-gathering" or bask in a daydream, sight and hearing are somewhat suspended. In deep anesthesia, in addition to the loss of information coming from the major sense organs, touch, pain, and organic sensations are also discontinued. Certainly as we prepare for sleep we do everything possible to reduce stimulation. We lie down so that our muscles can relax and close our eyes to shut out the exciting visual world. The rabbit lays back its efficient ears to exclude sound, while the human being seeks peace and repose in seclusion. If mental activity does not diminish we sometimes count sheep, relying upon the monotony of the counting process to blot out other more exciting stimuli. In this way the rocking of the cradle, the lapping of waves, the call of the katydid, the very rhythm by which day inevitably turns to night are for infant, sailor, farmer, and adult a summons to sleep.

There is an important practical lesson to be learned from these facts. The individual tired from "doing nothing" and the driver lulled to sleep by the tedium of the road on which he is driving dramatically illustrate the vital role our senses play, not only in providing the content of consciousness but in keeping us awake and tuned in. There was a remarkable case of a man in whom disease had eliminated almost all sensory channels but those of his internal organs and one eye. Upon closing the single functioning eye, he immediately fell asleep.

Whereas sensory stimuli provide the "fuel" for consciousness, the reticular formation is its warden. Buried in the center of the brain stem and sending its fingers into the lobes of the thalamus and into the

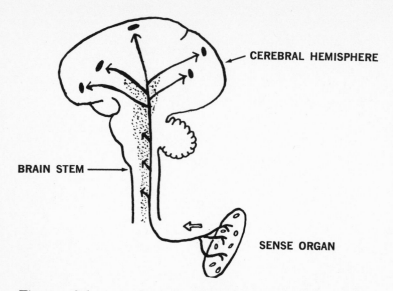

CEREBRAL HEMISPHERE

BRAIN STEM

SENSE ORGAN

Fig. 23 *Schematic drawing of the relationship of the major sensory tracts to the reticular formation (dotted area) and the cerebral cortex (Arrows show, in simplified form, how impulses from a sense organ are dispersed as they pass through the reticular formation.)*

hypothalamus, it is this intricate nerve network which guards the threshold to consciousness, which arouses us and signals the cortex that there is work to be done. We do not know how the sensory supply is actually controlled, but it is certain that the hard-working reticular system regulates the volume of its flow and plays a major role in determining the design of sensory patterns.

As the major sensory nerve trunks climb up through the brain stem toward the roof of the brain, they also send brushlike branches into the reticular formation (see Fig. 23). When stimulated, this central clearing station does not relay specific messages—the news of a ringing telephone, a hungry stomach, good food— to particular terminals in the cortex. Instead it spreads its signals over the brain above, rousing the cortex to wakefulness. Once alerted, it is for the cortex to determine that, specifically, the telephone is ringing and the meat roasting. At the same time the reticular system sends messages to other centers in the brain which, according to request, either excite or inhibit the muscular apparatus of the body.

By itself the reticular formation cannot produce consciousness, for it does not provide meaningful contact with the environment. Without this activating system, however, the mighty cortex would sleep on—deaf, dumb, blind, and numb to the call of even the most demanding message—for to be conscious we must first be awake.

In and Out of Focus

It is not sufficient to be awake. The general state of wakefulness must be maintained, and, more specifically, attention must be created and focused. Daily we perform many complicated acts of which we are only briefly and dimly conscious. We dress, eat, write, walk through crowded streets, drive cars, yet rarely give our full attention to what we are doing. The pianist who has mastered the notes of a musical composition ignores his fingers and concentrates on tone and phrasing. As the music weaves its spell, however, the player's thoughts may wander to scenes and events far beyond the room in which he sits or flee down the shadowy lanes and hidden alleys of the mind. Then, as a wayward finger stumbles, attention is immediately recalled from its roving and is returned to where, for the moment, it is most needed.

The focus of attention fluctuates subtly and swiftly, following dictates often so obscure and private that no one can discover their source. It is as if there were a searchlight playing across the human scene: All the raw material of consciousness is there, but only what the beam illumines receives our momentary attention; only what the recall system can bring forth from storage belongs to the consulting library of consciousness. One of Sigmund Freud's most important contributions was to recognize that events which exist in the shadows or the darkness beyond the spotlight of attention, events which we do not immediately or easily recall, nevertheless shape the development of our emotions and thoughts, and like the powerful, unseen pull of the moon on the earth quietly influence the patterns of human behavior.

Meanwhile we must admire the tremendous economy of a system in which simple, voluntary activities, once learned, are removed from the center of the stage and attend to themselves more or less automatically. Nor should we overlook the efficiency of a system in which the intermediate steps of creative activity occur in some unknown time and sequence within the antechambers of consciousness. The poet may compose his sonnet in what seems to be a sudden inspiration, for no one can reconstruct the course of the poem's "underground" preparation. Similarly, many a scientific discovery or insight appears to have been the gift of a dream or to have burst full-blown from sleep. Yet as every blossom must have its stem and roots, so too must insight and invention have their preparation. It is only that awareness need not attend the entire process.

Finally, we must be grateful for a system which guards our sanity, first by clearing the stage of meaningless clutter and second by not insisting that we remember everything we experience—by permitting us to forget. It is indeed a fortunate gift for a creature with a brain which also contains human memory. Forgetting—and the ability to modify what is remembered —is the priceless balm which soothes pain and dims sorrow so that man, sensitive and vulnerable, is somewhat protected from the suffering which is part of his human condition.

How the searchlight of attention operates or where it is located is still not known. Probably many levels of the human brain must participate before attention can be focused. As we have seen, it is the reticular formation which, in addition to waking us up and putting us to sleep, monitors the flow of sensory information. Unlike the other cells of the sensory system, there is some evidence that the neurons in the reticular network are capable of adapting to stimuli so that the sleeping city dweller is not disturbed by sounds of traffic but may, on the other hand, spend a wakeful night in the unfamiliar silence of the country.

The reticular formation is fed not only by sensory messages arriving from peripheral stations in the body but by the sophisticated electrical patterns from the cerebral cortex itself, which even in sleep maintains vigilance over the lower systems in the brain. By means of complex "round trip" connections with the brain stem, the cortex contributes indirectly to the maintenance of its own alertness. In addition, tangled circuits of traffic originating in the headquarters of emotion in the thalamus, hypothalamus, and the older cortex flow downstream to the reticular network. Ultimately motivation, mood, fear, and satisfaction play important roles in creating and focusing attention. A mother may sleep through a thunderstorm but will hear her baby's cry; you may not respond to screaming fire engines, but will awaken if your name is spoken. When you retire at night, the tension created by the anticipation of examinations and deadlines or by the persistence of unsolved problems may cause the higher centers of the brain to refuse the lower brain's sensible request for sleep.

Interlocking Systems

Consciousness resides, therefore, not in a cluster of privileged cells or in a hidden switch but in the meshing of several intricate systems. Despite independent duties, these systems must cooperate with such precision and delicate balance that they almost seem to interlock at the point where they create our awareness of the outer world and our inner selves. To be well tuned to reality human awareness requires the reticular system to sort and amplify the messages it receives and to keep the brain awake. In addition it needs the "precise" sensory system linking the body with the highest offices of the brain as well as those mysterious cortical areas which contain the archives of memory and the circuits of association that orient consciousness in time and space.

It has been suggested that disturbances in consciousness, from the most obvious to those which are almost undetectable, occur when any one of these systems is injured or disengaged so that it no longer cooperates with the rest of the mechanism. Sleep and anesthetics seem to involve primarily the reticular system and higher cortical levels. Although large parts of the cerebral cortex can be removed without producing loss of consciousness, injury to the brain stem may produce coma, either by interfering with metabolic centers which control the brain's vital supplies of oxygen and glucose or by jamming the dense, crowded nerve routes which carry the equally important flow of sensory "fuel" to the upper levels of the organ.

According to this hypothesis, dreaming, a more subtle alteration in consciousness, may be due to a decoupling of incoming sensory information from the memory and association arrangements in the higher brain. Because the sensory system is asleep, the inner patterns are in this way allowed to "free wheel." Presumably, mental disturbances, such as delusions and some hallucinations, result when sensory information arriving from the external environment is for some reason improperly matched with the patterns of past experience existing in upper centers of the brain. Thus the individual who suffers from unreasonable fears of persecution may feel as he does either because the sensory system has been depressed and is not doing its work or because higher centers of the brain have grown overactive and have become so satisfied with their own output that they no longer check with the state of affairs in the outside world.

One Third of Our Life

Sleep, that alteration of consciousness so familiar to each of us, is a mystery which has fascinated man from ancient times to the present. Yet modern science still knows little about sleep—why we sleep or what it is.

Primitive man regarded sleep as a temporary form of death caused each night by the escape of his spirit. His dreams were clear proof of his spirit's nocturnal adventures. In recent times it was believed that sleep occurred when blood flow to the brain decreased so that quietly, passively, the master organ was forced to diminish activity. It has also been suggested that sleep results from the accumulation in the blood of the chemical poisons of fatigue. Today we know that these explanations are incorrect, for blood flow to the brain does not decrease, and we may fall asleep even though we are not tired. On the other hand, when we are greatly fatigued sleep may elude us.

So essential to life is sleep that man and all higher animals lapse into unconsciousness and sleep for considerable portions of their lives although in drawing the curtain on their senses they often risk the very life they seek to preserve. Unfortunately sleep cannot be stored. It would be pleasant to sleep for long periods when it is convenient and draw on these reserves during extended wakeful periods, but nothing so practical is possible. The restorative powers of sleep are fleeting, perishable, and cannot be accumulated. Even animals which sleep through the winter in hibernation require regular periods of sleep during their active summer hours, for sleep is essential to the normal metabolism of the body. No matter how well it is fed and watered, an animal will die in a few days if deprived of sleep, and although no one knows the amount of sleeplessness fatal to the human being, we too must sleep if we are to live.

It appears that we sleep not so much for the sake of our muscles or other organs as to rest a tired brain. If we slept merely to permit fatigued muscles and bodily tissues to recover, we would expect to awaken refreshed and to be at our maximum efficiency in the morning.

Experiments have shown, however, that efficiency—which appears to be related to body temperature—is at a low ebb both before going to bed and upon awakening in the morning. Allowing for individual variations, it reaches its peak during the middle part of the waking period.

Many experiments have been conducted to determine how long a person can stay awake and to observe the effects of as much as four to five days of artificial wakefulness. Lack of sleep does not cause significant changes in heart rate or in blood pressure but takes its heaviest toll on the nervous system. Sleep is apparently a reparative process which cannot occur within the central nervous system while it is active.

People forced experimentally to remain awake become increasingly irritable and silly, emotionally unstable, and even experience hallucinations. They suffer from memory loss, find it difficult to concentrate, are sluggish in shifting attention, and are slow and inaccurate in performing long tasks—symptoms all too familiar to most of us. Deprived of sleep, a person can force himself to perform, but, for example, the effort consumed in solving an arithmetic problem is about three times as great as it would be in a subject who was permitted to sleep.

How much sleep do we need? The amount of sleep required varies with individuals and is also affected by age. The newborn infant sleeps eighteen to twenty hours a day; thereafter the amount declines through adolescence. Most adults sleep seven to nine hours, older persons are satisfied with five to seven hours of sleep, and women usually require more sleep than men. However, as anyone knows who has awakened "exhausted" after a full night of sleep, restful sleep is determined not only by the number of hours we remain in bed but by the quality and depth of sleep as well. A few hours of sound sleep may be more valuable than many hours of light, fitful slumber. Cheerful, strongly motivated individuals who are interested in what they are doing can often work efficiently with small amounts of sleep. Similarly, you may fall asleep while engaged in tedious work but will stay up all night to complete a task which is interesting and challenging. Drugs, fear, incentive, and boredom may all modify the extent to which we feel fatigue. If you dangle a silver trophy in front of the brain which drives exhausted muscles, those muscles will find the resources for just one more sprint.

Sleeping and Waking

In sleep all the senses are not uniformly suppressed, nor does sleep envelop us in a solid blanket of unconsciousness, for the depth of sleep varies. Normally it is greatest at the end of the first hour. After that it decreases sharply from the second to the third hour and more slowly thereafter until waking. In adults there is sometimes a second period of deep sleep during the fifth and sixth hours; in children this second phase is usually found between the eighth and ninth hours. One theory states that people with cheerful morning dispositions, "morning people," are those who attain deepest sleep by the end of the first hour, whereas "evening people" reach their maximum intensity of sleep relatively slowly, perhaps two to three hours after falling asleep. Dreams occur during light sleep, particularly during the period before waking; deep sleep is dreamless. People who maintain that they do not dream are deceived. Probably they awaken rapidly and instead of savoring the patterns of the night for even a few seconds they quickly fill their minds with concrete thoughts belonging to the waking world and never remember their dreams.

We are not born with a need to sleep at night but are only gradually conditioned to sleep during the dark, quiet hours. Animals and infants sleep in briefer periods scattered through a twenty-four-hour cycle, often waking only long enough to attend to basic needs. The rabbit, for example, is kept awake only by urgent sensations such as hunger, thirst, the need to mate and to eliminate wastes—"wakefulness of necessity." To many observers the evolutionary development of sleep suggests that sleep, rather than wakefulness, may be the "natural" state. The mystery is then not how we sleep but how we stay awake. According to one of the most fascinating theories of sleep, as the cerebral cortex develops in higher animals, a "wakefulness of choice" is added to this primitive "wakefulness of necessity." Compared to the rabbit, the dog takes a greater interest in his surroundings. He has learned to play, can be trained to work, and to do both he stays awake. Monkeys and apes, with their lively curiosity and eager desire for communication, devote still less time to sleep. Finally, man, who always has "miles to go before he sleeps," who is all too poignantly aware of the limited time he has in which to embrace his world, normally sleeps during a single period, often reluctantly, and then only as long as is physiologically necessary.

The mechanism of the sleep-waking equilibrium is at present unknown. Physiologists have discovered two antagonistic centers in the brain: a "sleep center" located in the thalamus including connections to the hypothalamus, midbrain and cortex; a "waking center" in the reticular formation of the midbrain and in the hypothalamus. Normally these centers cooperate, by means which still elude us, to maintain the balance of the sleep-waking rhythm. As we have seen, the cortex, the home of ambition, worry, bright ideas and interesting thoughts, may temporarily interfere with this rhythm, but in the end the primitive brain must have its way: We must sleep. It is simple enough to speak of a sleep or waking center, but this does not explain the mystery of sleep. The relationship between these two centers is so complex and so poorly understood that it still has not been determined whether true sleep results from the stimulation of a sleep center or from the inhibition of a waking center.

It is widely believed today that sleep begins when the number of impulses streaming into the cerebral cortex is greatly reduced. It is not so much fatigue which puts us to sleep, as we noted earlier, but rather a definite set of conditions which discourage stimulation and excitement. As we approach the mysterious border which divides the realms of wakefulness and sleep, our muscles relax, breathing slows, and many bodily activities are reduced to lower levels, while the cells of the reticular system cooperate by cutting down the flow of sensory traffic. The mother sings softly to her child and rocks him in her arms; we close our eyes and lull ourselves with mild, monotonous thoughts. The tired cortex relaxes its vigilance; thoughts begin to wander and then cease altogether. As the last sheep goes over the fence and—with the fence—disappears in midair, we are in that moment asleep.

At present sleep has surrendered few of its secrets and its exact physiology still remains unknown. Sometimes shallow, at other times profound, sleep obeys predictable biological rhythms and yet bends to the shape of individual personality. At one moment it is vacant as oblivion, and in the next it is landscaped with the weird, drifting scenery of dreams and populated with strange, distorted images. Its depths are unfathomable, but in the quiet shoals along its banks inspiration and insight occasionally appear like precious gems washed from the mysterious recesses of the sleeper's brain.

Although it is an interruption of consciousness, sleep is not a passive running down of activity but is instead a highly complex, organized state in which many levels of the nervous system coordinate to turn us off, to accompany us safely through the unconscious hours, and finally to restore us, renewed and refreshed, to the waking scene. Between sunset and sunrise we are senseless for a number of hours. Yet the patterns of the previous day are never severed. They are carried below the surface of consciousness, emerging on the waking shore, subtly altered by the alchemy of time, but recognizable and ready to thread their way into the new day. Thus does the nerve cell, that impermanent collection of dancing molecules and atoms, mysteriously weave the rich tapestry of human consciousness.

9

"PROGRAMMING" THE BRAIN

Intelligent, clever, impudent, in body and limb disturbingly like ourselves, the chimpanzee romping in the zoo and the gorilla sulking in his cage draw us irresistibly, for they are caricatures of the human pattern. In the modern ape is preserved, as in any fossil, the promise of the human brain and mind, which long before the coming of man was crudely sketched in his prehuman ancestors. Although he is not on the main line of our descent, the living ape suggests what that early brain might have been like. Above all it is in the gap between what an ape is not and what a man is that we seek an understanding of what it means to be a human being.

Man is an animal who has discovered himself, who thinks, reasons, plans, and creates, and who communicates by means of language. He knows right from wrong, feels pity, and grants mercy; he pays taxes, controls his emotions, and has invented clocks and calendars. Yet animals much below him on the evolutionary scale learn and remember, make plans, solve problems, calculate, and even reason. The lowly worm advancing through the stem of a Y-shaped tube learns to avoid the left branch of the device if it receives an electric shock every time it moves in that direction. The lesson "Bear right!" taught by this experience must be recorded at least briefly in a primitive memory system. The fish and eagle pursuing their prey calculate and plan, and the dog trying to escape from a cage eventually discovers the latch and, providing the position of the latch is not changed, uses it promptly in the future. The ape, asked to solve a similar problem, actually reasons his way to freedom. Instead of hurling himself aimlessly about his cage as the dog does, he stops to study the problem. Having learned previously not only that a *particular* latch opens the door, but, more generally, that *latches open doors*, the ape understands what it is he must do and proceeds to search intelligently for the latch no matter how often its position in the cage is changed.

Since intelligence is an evasive quality, authorities who seek to capture and measure it in an I.Q. test readily admit that they are not always certain what it is they have measured or if, indeed, an individual's performance in solving problems or in perceiving relationships is an accurate indication of his intelligence. The intelligence quotient (I.Q.) is simply a ratio or a score which relates the subject's performance on standard testing material to that of hundreds of other subjects who have taken the same test.

There are many definitions of intelligence. It has

been called the ability to "perceive relationships," "to learn how to learn," and "all-round intellectual ability." However it is defined, man differs from the most cunning and teachable animal in that he is more intelligent. His brain has a greater capacity to learn and remember, and using this knowledge he reasons, imagines, and creates with a skill and facility possessed by no other kind of brain. Indeed, the burnt child, like the burnt animal, fears the fire—but only briefly. Long ago when early man, nursing his painful fingers, first learned the basic lesson *fire is hot: fire burns*, his lively curiosity and intelligence did not let the matter rest there. Contemplating this information, he next observed the useful properties of fire, sought the means by which to render it friend, not foe, and then squatting in his cave before its bright, comforting flames, instructed his children in the lessons of fire. Many thousands of years later, still pursuing this adventure, the descendents of the early fire-tamer were to harness the energy in the nucleus of the atom and in the solar furnace which burns in the sun above.

Any attempt to explain the highest attributes of the human brain, to penetrate its supreme mysteries, must be accompanied by a deep sense of humility and considerable concern that theories be recognized as the brilliant speculations of devoted scientists but not necessarily as facts. We have not yet found the residence of memory, the home of judgment, nor isolated the physiological properties of intelligence; no one has charted the neural path of an idea or located the well-springs of imagination. Although we know much about the way in which we learn and remember, we have found only the vaguest clues to the actual chemical and physical changes in our brain cells and in their connections which are wrought by learning and its partner, memory. Comparisons with man-made "brains," the electronic computers, have also suggested possible parallel mechanisms in the human nervous system. For the most part, scientists can only venture theories, still unverified, of how a brain learns, remembers, and thinks.

How We Learn

Learning and its preservation as memory are the raw materials from which we construct our thoughts, the equivalent of the information and instructions with which the computer is "programmed." It is important to point out, however, that the higher primates, particularly man, also learn by thinking. The precious gift of speech has provided man with a system by which he can lock thoughts and abstract ideas in the symbolic form of words. In this form they are more easily stored and manipulated. The child learns by a process of trial and error that fire burns. Next he is taught that the word—or symbol—which describes this experience is "hot." Later when he is told that the radiator, the stove, and his dinner are also "hot" although they emit no flame, he concludes without further experiment that they will hurt him and he leaves them alone. In this case the conclusion drawn from the reasoning process, in which old associations are arranged in new patterns, is itself the lesson learned.

If we define learning as *a change in the pattern of an individual's behavior as the result of his personal experience and reactions*, then it is true that all animals, even the one-celled protozoa, learn. But they learn neither as much nor as efficiently as we do. Ironically, in the extreme helplessness of human infancy lies the key to our ultimate competence as adults. For although the human brain is born with its full supply of basic units, it is at birth so little wired and committed that we are completely dependent on others to protect and to educate us. From the beginning the brain is programmed and its circuits are patterned in the rich social, cultural, and personal environment created by other human brains. But the mere possession of information is insufficient. In a practical sense it is neither the rate of learning nor its extent which is the banner of intelligence but rather our ability to use what we have learned. The human memory machines who star in quiz programs are not necessarily intelligent. Accumulations of knowledge are required for thinking, but the sign of intelligence is the way this information is used, not its sheer poundage.

The manner in which animals and human beings learn has been extensively studied by psychologists. There are many different kinds of learning. Its actual categories vary from one system of classification to the next and will not be considered in detail here. Man, more than any other animal, uses not one or another method of learning but employs various techniques in complex and subtle combinations.

By a simple process of association the infant learns that his mother means food and other pleasant experiences, or the school child learns that for all practical purposes 1492 belongs to Columbus. A great part of learning, particularly in animals, is accomplished by the slow, fumbling, ultimately effective process known as *trial-and-error learning*. In this method the animal or person attempts to solve a problem by trying many possible solutions, disregarding the failures—providing life and limb have not been sacrificed—and remembering the successful solution. Through repetition and practice we learn to walk and talk and tie our shoe laces, and it is in this way that our conditioned reflexes and habits are established. In Pavlov's dogs the inborn reflex of salivation in the presence of food was so conditioned that the animals' mouths watered at the sound of a bell even though food was no longer present. Pavlov's dogs are a simple example. Human conditioning can become extremely complex, and we are often unaware of the routes taken by our conditioned responses and our associations. It is difficult to point to the origins of prejudice, of irrational fears, and of many of our intuitions which probably derive from the unseen linkages and lessons of our earlier years. Sometimes, despite limitations in qualifications, we choose a man for a job purely on a "hunch," never realizing how much he reminds us of a much admired friend or parent whose competence was long ago proven.

There is another kind of learning, sometimes called learning by *insight*, or *understanding what to do*. However, the relationship between this more sophisticated form of learning and the clumsier trial-and-error method is not always clear; frequently they work together. Essentially, learning by insight refers to a method of solving a problem in which the subject summons appropriate facts and previous associations and mentally rearranges them in new and useful relationships. This kind of learning may be very rapid and depends heavily on the symbolic system provided by language. Once there was a boy who dropped a coin through a grid in the sidewalk. Sadly he studied the situation. All of a sudden he had a "bright idea." Attaching a piece of chewing gum to a length of string, he lowered his invention through the grating and retrieved his coin. The boy used his knowledge of the sticky properties of gum, the "reaching" properties of string, perhaps earlier associations with fishing lines, and solved his problem by using reasoning and imagination.

From its lowest to its loftiest levels, learning involves much more than the haphazard storage of a particular response to a single stimulus. Specifically, learning is the power to abstract, to grasp those qualities which are similar in a situation; ultimately it is the force which imposes order and meaning upon the chaos of experience. Thus we recognize a chair as a chair from whatever angle we view it, and whether we see it or only touch it. We recognize a letter of print no matter how its size and type-face are varied. We know lions as lions, fish as fish, men as men, and even the four-year-old child realizes that fish, lions, and men have qualities in common which do not belong to chairs.

It is logical to expect that when learning occurs the brain must in some way be altered by its experience. It has long been believed that use and disuse influence the readiness of the synaptic junctions to transmit impulses across the gap which separates nerve cells. This suggests that the repetition which is part of the learning process eventually leaves a lasting change in the nerve route so that a particular pattern, perhaps that for shooting a basketball or reciting a poem, is more easily replayed the next time it is needed.

For many years scientists sought without success to demonstrate those physical and chemical changes etched into our nervous system by the process of learning. Recently there has been some encouraging work in this field. Scientists have reported finding an increase in the weight of the rat's cerebral cortex as the result of learning as well as an increase in certain chemicals known to be involved in the transmission of nerve impulses across the synaptic junction. In other experiments actual changes at the synaptic junctions have been found following learning. There is also some evidence that as repeated impulses fire along the length of a nerve axon, they stimulate the growth and branching of the terminal endings of the fiber, thus continuing the task of "wiring" the brain and cultivating its intricate tracery until in the wealth of its interconnections it surpasses anything we might build or even imagine.

Libraries of the Mind

Learning and memory are intimately related processes, for if each day we had to relearn all the skills and information acquired the day before, if a night's sleep wiped the slate clean, if from moment to moment the traces of experience dissolved, learning would be useless.

The dimensions of human memory are truly dazzling. The memory capacity of today's most able electronic computers is about two million units of information. The actual storage capacity of the human brain has never been measured, although it has been estimated that during our lifetime we store about ten times more information than is contained in all the books in the Library of Congress. The computing machine, when requested, releases its information in the same form in which it was originally stored. Human memory is far more subtle, inaccurate, and perishable. It has been pointed out that there is a difference between the recording system by which an event is impressed upon the nervous system and the recall system by which a memory is summoned from storage. Whether an experience is recorded in the first place depends upon a variety of factors which influence the condition of our nerve cells: age, alcohol, drugs, injuries which interfere with electrical activity, as well as interest, motivation and the level of attention. An elderly person may recall with ease the details of his childhood home, for these facts were recorded at a time when his nerve cells were in good condition and did their work efficiently. The same person nevertheless may not remember conversing with you only a few hours earlier, for his aged and worn recording apparatus has failed to preserve the trace of the recent experience.

When you record a piece of information in your brain, you have no guarantee that you will be able to recall it at will. Unpleasant experiences may be filed in impenetrable compartments, lying there potent but forgotten until coaxed from hiding by means of hypnosis, drugs, or special psychiatric techniques which summon related associations to turn the key in the mental lock. Other vivid but forgotten memories may be unexpectedly evoked by an experience once intimately linked with the original event. A drifting melody may stir a forgotten heartache, and the taste of a special dish dear to childhood may cause an adult to relive with all his senses and emotions fragments of scenes long ago buried in the past. Frequently we use artificial stimuli to stir a sluggish memory. The string tied around a finger as a reminder to bring home a loaf of bread helps to isolate this rather uninspiring memorandum from the vast clutter of images and thoughts floating through our heads. We depend upon rhyme to remind us that "in 1492 *Columbus* sailed the ocean blue," and in order to quote the last line of a poem we often must run through all the lines which precede it and to which it is linked.

At all times, attention, interest, and motivation are the powerful monitors of human memory. They influence what is to be preserved and what is to be overlooked; what is to be readily available and what is to remain buried in the subterranean vaults of memory. Thus we forget what is trivial, what is painful or embarrassing, and what originally was poorly recorded.

We use our memories to preserve various kinds of information. Although we may not think of it as memory, we possess, first of all, a memory for skilled acts. Through practice and repetition the nervous system learns how far a finger must stretch and curve to reach from one letter to the next on the typewriter, how much pressure to exert when holding an egg so that it does not break, and how to synchronize the movements of muscles in order to walk smoothly, run swiftly, and ride a bicycle.

We also remember the names and meanings of objects—that a chair has a basic shape, a certain use, and is represented by the word "chair." Language has put at man's disposal a vast body of information which he need never experience directly. A visitor from the tropics who has never seen snow may nevertheless recognize it from the descriptions of others.

Finally, we remember experiences, both recent and past. A fairly complete picture of each day's events is retained at least briefly in the superficial files of memory. In more permanent form are preserved the fragments of an important day many years gone: the setting, faces, conversations, the emotions we felt at the time, and the thoughts we thought. It is in remembering our personal experiences that the greatest discrepancy between what was recorded and what is recalled occurs. Generally, what we call a memory is not a duplicate record of the original experience. The memory of your fourth birthday party may consist of a blur of balloons, a partial guest list, a few details of furniture, and one or two of the feelings you experienced. But there is evidence that a more complete story of that party has been recorded somewhere in your brain, that the storehouse of memory is not as leaky as the recall system would make it appear.

In an interesting series of experiments performed on conscious patients undergoing brain surgery, it has been possible to tap what may well be the master recordings of memory. When certain areas of the temporal lobes are stimulated with an electrode, it is possible to summon memories which are of special

interest because they contain the emotions and inter-
pretations which accompanied the original experience.
As soon as the electrode is lifted, the "forced" memory
is lost. Unlike memory voluntarily recalled, in which
your first-grade teacher, as you remember her today, is
actually a generalization—a composite of memories
altered and aged by the passage of time—these artificially evoked experiences are single recollections and
appear to reproduce the original event as the subject
experienced it and edited it at the time. It is as if the
electrode had stumbled upon the original strip of
camera film, complete with its sound track and the
feelings and reactions which accompanied the opening
performance.

Even the ordinary experiences of our daily lives indicate that although we do not recall all that we have
stored, somewhere in the brain the information must
be available in the form in which it was originally recorded. We may find it difficult to recall the exact
appearance of a long-forgotten acquaintance, yet upon
meeting him once again, not only do we recognize him
immediately, but we note in detail the changes—
wrinkles, receding hairline, increased weight—which
have occurred in the intervening years. In some way
the new experience is immediately compared with
the neural records of the old experience, which, although buried, are not lost. The entire process of finding the old records, of sorting and comparing, of
judging similarities and differences, is so swift and

efficient that ordinarily we take this superbly organized filing system for granted.

Forgetting

The rate of forgetting is most rapid in its early stages, and it appears that it is the period immediately following an experience which is crucial for the "setting" of the memory trace. A severe blow on the head may leave past memory intact but may erase the memory of those events which occurred a few hours prior to the injury. It is almost as if the mark of these lost experiences had not had sufficient time to be permanently set. In more ordinary circumstances competing activities, rather than a physical blow, may interfere with those mysterious processes by which memory recognizes and classifies the material it plans to preserve. For this reason, at the time we are making the original recording we try to isolate the information and prevent it from running together with background events. It is difficult to study effectively if you are preoccupied with exciting weekend plans. An inability to remember a person's name may mean you failed to register it in the first place. Thus we are urged to "pay attention" when being introduced to someone and to concentrate long enough to make a mental note of the name and information we wish to retain. Similarly, "cramming" may achieve the immediate goal of passing an examination, but in the long run it is a waste of time. The memory traces made by this technique are superficial and fleeting; they are here today but gone tomorrow. Human memory, remarkable and enduring as it is, requires exclamation points and paragraphing, order and spacing; it cannot handle too much information in too short a time.

Circuits of Memory

For all that is known about the way in which memories are formed and forgotten, modern science knows very little about how nerve cells store information and nothing about the cerebral processes which search the files and facilitate its recall. We may manipulate the memory system as a whole, we may even cut out large sections of the cortex without destroying memory permanently, but we know of no selective way to locate the recording of a forgotten phone number or the notes of a sonata, or to erase the memory trace of a specific anxiety or grief. We must first wrest the secrets of memory from our brain tissue if we are to understand the far more complex problem of how the brain uses information to create thoughts—whether they be such petty decisions as what to wear or do next or those great creative insights by which primitive man conceived of fire as his friend and a modern genius, Einstein, perceived the relationships among the apparently separate physical phenomena of the universe.

However it operates, wherever are hidden the

multiplication tables, the faces of friends, the cata-
logues of pleasure and pain, it is clear that human
memory requires space. No single region of the brain
could possibly serve as the specialized storehouse of
memory. It has been estimated that millions of neurons
are involved in the recall of a single memory, for so
intricate is the storage system that each bit of information is itself broken into smaller pieces and stored at
different points in the brain. The color, shape, texture,
taste, meaning, feeling, and other associations which
belong to the word "apple" are scattered like the pieces
of a jigsaw puzzle throughout the storage units of the
brain. Yet upon request they spring together so that
immediately the familiar fruit is seen drifting across
a mental screen, hanging with companions in a mental
orchard, or resting in a fruit bowl similarly conjured
from the scattered fragments of a memory mosaic.

Strangely enough the massive frontal lobes at the
prow of the brain, so much concerned with the shaping
of personality, do not seem to be primarily involved
in the storage of memory. Electrical probes of the
temporal lobes, in which memories are artificially
pried from the brain, indicate that these regions between the temples and the ears are concerned with
memory. Although the interpretation of the evidence
remains controversial, it does appear that while the
temporal lobes may not be the actual archives of
memory, they are concerned with its recording mechan-

ism and certainly seem to have special access to the information stored in the scattered libraries of our memory.

Any theory which suggests how memory might be preserved must first contend with certain practical matters. Even in code form, memory cannot simply be deposited in a nerve cell, nor can its trace be assigned an exclusive nerve route, for the ten billion nerve cells in our cortex would hardly be sufficient to contain the almost three hundred billion, billion units of information which is one estimate of the memory capacity of the brain during an average lifetime. Furthermore, large areas of the cortex may be removed or damaged without causing obvious memory loss. This suggests that memory may have duplicate storage points. As the search for memory leads down into the subterranean world of the neuron's molecular structure, where millions of molecules are available for storage depots, scientists must still explain how memory can be preserved for years by a particle of matter which does not survive more than a day.

It is conceivable that certain memories might be "kept alive" in the form of a message which continues to circulate around a closed chain of nerve cells. Reverberating circuits of this type would eventually cause a cerebral traffic jam of incredible proportions and would not account for those enduring memories, habits, and conditioned reflexes which persist despite the interruption of the cycling activity by sleep, anesthesia, and concussion. Today there is evidence that eventually these self-firing messages as well as direct volleys of impulses fired by the repetition of a stimulus mark a lasting route so that long after the original activity has ceased, long after its electrical impulses have died away, we still recall events, emotions, and melodies; we still remember how to kiss and hold a spoon.

Although no one has ever seen a memory trace, it is believed that the trace is created when a group of cells, as the result of repeated stimulation, becomes part of a "cell-assembly" which discharges as a unit when signaled. A single neuron, depending upon its life history and how it has been "trained," participates in many such assemblies and in some way "knows" the other units to which it is assigned. Thus when you see or hear the word "mother," thousands of neurons immediately contribute their part of the pattern which flashes the familiar face on your mental screen. At the same time the replaying of one particular memory trace directly and indirectly bombards other neurons which take up the call and in discharging set loose a vast panorama of shifting subpatterns giving to human memory its unique richness and depth. Swiftly the image of mother is followed by that of father, perhaps by a view of yourself, by a name, a song, a scene, and by the many other intricate associations filed and cross-referenced in your personal records under "mother."

As we have seen, specific memories are not stored as single units, nor are they filed in one place in the brain. That a memory is first dismantled and its components dispersed throughout the cells of the brain, that it does not "put all its eggs in one basket," may help to explain memory's uncanny ability to survive the destruction of considerable amounts of brain territory. If certain storage points fail to report or if they provide incorrect information, the missing or false responses may be offset or drowned out by other answers which are correct. What is more, we do not need all the pieces of a puzzle in order to recognize the picture.

It is important to understand that it is not the anatomical pathway of the actual memory trace which endures as memory. Instead it is the master recording, the *pattern* of the trace, which is broken into parts and stored and which contains the instructions for timing and tuning the circuits of a specific memory. Therefore when they are properly directed, nerve cells not involved in establishing the original memory can reduplicate the memory trace.

In many ways memory resembles an alphabet. Just as the rich fabric of the English language is created from the complex arrangements of a mere twenty-six letters, memory, rather than storing each experience as a specific symbol, relies upon a flexible system of interchangeable parts which may be arranged and rearranged in endless patterns of meaning and behavior according to a master design. Some of these parts are very old, some more recently acquired, but each of us, according to individual inclination and ability, is free to draw upon this vast reservoir. We hold a baseball bat with the grasping movement originally learned for picking up and holding a rattle, and we write stories about flying carpets and the inhabitants of Mars and understand the thoughts and feelings of other human being by recombining the bits and pieces of our own experience. Needless to say it is the "master design," the stored blueprint of a memory, which determines the specific form in which you remember last summer's vacation. However, the details of that vacation— weather, sand, friends, and events—and, in turn, still smaller fragments of these details are not rigidly limited to a single memory but are now free to flavor and enrich those experiences which are yet to come and those which already are memory.

Molecules of Memory

How experience leaves its mark upon our nerve cells is still largely unknown. Brilliant work in the past decade has at last unearthed a few clues to the puzzle, but as yet the full story of memory remains to be told. We have already noted that use and disuse influence the behavior of the synaptic junctions, which in their strategic positions as traffic policemen play an important role in directing the flow of neural travel.

It is now believed that memory may be stored in the large, complex protein molecules which are the basic structural units of all living cells, "the stones of which the house of life is built." Each nerve cell contains millions of these chainlike protein molecules, which in turn consist of subunits called *amino acids*, hundreds of which are linked in a specific sequence along the molecule. Although there are only about twenty different kinds of amino acids, the number of ways in which these protein building blocks may be combined is practically endless. Since protein molecules are readily changed by electrical impulses or by chemical substances such as alcohol, it is possible that experience may be recorded in our nervous system by alterations in the structure of these giant protein molecules upon which are engraved, from birth to death, the joys and sorrows, facts and fancies of our personal history.

But the matter is not so simple. Since the life span of a protein molecule may be no more than a single day, it has been necessary to explain how the records of memory can be preserved for years despite the loss of the original storage units. Molecular biologists searching for the secret of life and for the key to the genetic code determining which cells are to be skin cells, which nerve cells, and which collections of cells are to be horses and which people, made an important discovery. They found that certain giant protein molecules are capable of reproducing themselves and that the specific structure of a protein molecule is controlled by other complex molecules called *nucleic acids*. DNA (deoxyribonucleic acid) and its companion RNA (ribonucleic acid) are two of these vital cell chemicals which carry the instructions for hooking together the amino acids of the protein molecule. Following the ingenious code provided by its nucleic acids, the protein molecule can manufacture exact or nearly exact copies of itself. It is possible that in the self-duplicating protein molecule, its structure subtly but relentlessly altered by the inroads of experience, may lie part of the secret of how our memories are stored and perpetuated.

Since a change in the nucleic acid will result in an altered protein molecule, it is apparent that DNA and RNA molecules are responsible not only for the accuracy with which genetic information is transmitted from one generation to the next but for the reliability with which memories are transferred from molecule to molecule. Throughout the years of your life the untold numbers of molecular "notches" which correspond to your first day in school must be handed down from one protein molecule to another according to a pattern entrusted to their complex nucleic acids. It is little wonder, then, that in the whirring molecular factories which from moment to moment and from an infinite number of submicroscopic parts recreate the seemingly permanent YOU, time and chance nibble away at the records of memory and refashion its contents much as the unremitting sea reshapes the shores it drains.

10

THE THINKING ANIMAL

No one knows how patterns of electrical activity are converted into thoughts, ideas, and feelings or, for that matter, how an idea can trigger a flow of electrical impulses through the nervous system. From charges of electrical energy produced by the sight or the sound of the word *man*, the brain in some unknown way extracts a great variety of meanings and a series of mental photographs associated with that word. Granting this formidable gap between electrons and experience, we may still describe what thinking does and try to imagine the cerebral circuits along which our thoughts must be presumed to travel.

Just as a melody is a sequence of notes in time, a thought is a sequence of memories arranged in a pattern which, for the thinker at least, is new. Thinking is the process by which the previously stored input of the brain—knowledge—is summoned and then rearranged to reveal new relationships. Although we need not be consciously aware of it, our thoughts no matter how insignificant, have purpose, direction, and control. The reasoning process by which we relate a cause to its effect in order to solve problems or make judgments may be extremely logical, but it is not always necessary that we be conscious of the logic underlying our conclusions or even that our thoughts be reasonable and our reasoning logical.

The flow of images and feelings through our dreams, the dissolving patterns of fantasy, or the shifting kaleidoscope of vaguely connected memory pictures during idle reveries, while not to be called reasoning, are nevertheless a form of thinking. Furthermore, although words do play an important role in expressing our inner thoughts, not all thinking or even reasoning need be verbal. People vary in this respect: Some are primarily verbal thinkers; others may rely on complex visual or auditory symbols as well. But in all cases, whether in spinning dreams or solving mathematical problems, a discovery is made, a problem is solved, or at least our memory cards are selected and shuffled to produce new designs. Much of a day's thinking is not consciously directed, whereas much of what we consider thinking is not thinking at all. When we say, "I am trying to think of that date," we are not really thinking. It would be more accurate to say, "I am trying to remember that date," for in this case there is no new arrangement of memory, only the recall of a fact.

Of all creatures man has the greatest capacity for learning and the greatest ability to use his knowledge to meet his needs—needs which are no longer limited to basic biological drives. Man must eat and drink, sleep and mate, but he is also driven to know himself, to tame the physical world, to distinguish good and evil, to create beauty, and to revere and worship what he regards as divine. Creative, restless, reverent, and thoughtful, there is nothing else on earth, animal or machine, quite like him.

The superior intelligence of the human being is believed to depend not on a special kind of brain or on neurons of privileged design, but rather on vast reserves of nerve cells and the intricacy of their branches and interconnections. It has been estimated that the number of potential connections available to the ten billion cells of the human cortex would be a number so large that it would take about two thousand pages of an ordinary book to print it. In the quantity and complexity rather than the quality of the brain's basic units lay the road down from the trees and into laboratories and libraries, factories, and concert halls.

Patterns of Thought

As far as nerve cells are concerned, what and how we think are determined at any given moment by the brain's immediate and very recent input as well as by its inherited and acquired structural characteristics. Let us see what this means. Seeing the word "mother" printed here may provide the immediate input for a train of thoughts concerning your mother. In addition, her recent censure or praise may have left a cycle of

impulses reverberating in your brain which unques-
tionably flavor and direct your present thoughts about
her. The "mother-stimulus," however, does not enter
a blank nervous system. At birth your nerve cells already possess certain physiological endowments, admittedly unknown, which influence the "style" and
manner in which you will think later on. A person who
is blind from birth thinks about "mother" without
even the memory of a visual image of her; the dull,
stupid person may react to the stimulus with few
patterns of response, whereas the brilliant, creative
individual may react with an outburst of rich and colorful thoughts, as impulses flowing along old "mother-
routes" suddenly set out in new and original directions.
Finally, your past experience—your habits, knowledge,
and attitudes as registered in your nerve cells and at
their connections—will influence the thoughts which
now find their way along the channels of your brain.
Your ability to picture your mother, to imagine her
voice, her frown, and her smile, depends on data already stored in your memory files. To put it starkly,
your thoughts will be associated with love or loneliness,
joy or bitterness, depending on whether you were
raised in a happy or an unhappy home.

Because man is truly a thinking animal, because he
understands complex relationships, because he reasons,
imagines, and creates, he has become the dominant
species on the earth. This raises a most tantalizing

question: What qualities distinguish the exceptional human brain and what is the physiology of creativity and genius?

The word "genius" is one of the most misused terms in our language. It is not a compliment to be loosely bestowed, nor is it a synonym for "talent." Studies of genius are many and its description and definition vary. We cannot dissect a brain and find the attributes of genius within it. We do not know why many geniuses are born to ordinary parents, nor does a lofty I.Q. seem to be a guarantee of genius. It is probably safe to say that the genius is a person who is not only highly endowed with intelligence but who is born with unique and extraordinary creative powers. In addition, his emotional climate is one in which these creative drives may bear fruit.

Whether a genius is moody and withdrawn in disposition or sunny and sociable does not seem to be of primary significance. Although it is impossible to supply a personality formula for genius, creative giants do seem to share certain qualities: freedom from conventional beliefs and routine patterns of thinking, a willingness to consider new possibilities no matter how bizarre or unlikely, and added to this gift of a truly "open mind," the power of sustained concentration and persistence. When asked how he made his discoveries, Sir Isaac Newton answered, "By always thinking into them." Charles Darwin gave similar credit to a free mind and unswerving dedication to the problems which absorbed him. The urge to create, to solve a problem, to bring something to completion—and the misery and tension which attend the denial of these potent drives—may well be the forces which drove Alexander to conquer his worlds, Michelangelo to carve his marble, and Galileo to follow his stars. And in kind, at least, they are the same forces which impel us to find the solutions to unsolved problems, to complete difficult assignments, and to pursue with courage and concentration those goals in life on which we have set our hearts and minds.

It is easier to describe genius than to define it. Genius has been called a "superior power of seeing," "the highest conceivable form of original ability" and "an extraordinary capacity to perceive analogies not readily apparent to the ordinary mind." The last definition is interesting because the ability to perceive resemblances is fundamental to the process of thinking, from its most elementary to its most exalted levels. As thinking becomes more inventive, the nature of the relationships we discover becomes more original. Thus the rat can be taught to identify a variety of designs which possess in common a square shape. The child, at a higher level of intelligence, grasps the concept of "tenness" common to ten fingers, ten apples, and the number "10." The boy who retrieves his dime from beneath the sidewalk grating makes the observation, original to him, that fishing rod and hook are related to fish as string and gum are to his lost coin. Galileo, the great Italian astronomer, discovered the similarity between a lamp swinging in the Cathedral of Pisa and the oscillations of a pendulum. In an extraordinary scientific insight Einstein pointed out the relationship among such seemingly unrelated phenomena as matter, energy, motion, and time.

Often this illumination or insight appears unexpectedly, arriving at the edges of sleep, in dreams, and in other unguarded moments. The great mathematician Poincaré solved a difficult problem while getting into a taxi to go to the opera; the Greek mathematician Archimedes made a useful discovery while stepping into the bathtub; Kekule conceived the benzene ring in a dream. And your "brain storm" may occur as you awaken in the morning or at some other unlikely moment of the day.

This does not mean that great and small ideas drop as gifts from the gods into empty heads. Inspiration comes only to a brain which has done its "homework" —a brain which has been primed with the information needed to solve a problem and has sorted and evaluated that information. It does seem true, however, that creative ideas and new relationships are more readily discovered when the traditional techniques of thinking and of perceiving are relaxed. Freed of a conscious driver, the brain is then allowed to examine problems from a fresh angle, to juggle their components, and to experiment with more improbable but original comparisons and relationships. It is for this reason that it is wise to take a holiday from a stubborn problem, to allow time and a change of scene to dissolve a focus which has become rigid and which, in solidifying, has limited the kinds of thoughts the brain will tolerate. When later we return to the problem with a fresh approach, we may discover—to give a simple illustration—not the specific, elusive words needed to repair an awkward line but that the problem is more simply solved by rephrasing the entire sentence.

An Idea Is Born

Although the psychological setting in which creative thoughts are best nurtured has been well studied, no one has ever observed images and ideas circulating through the networks of the brain or a cause in pursuit of its effect; nor has anyone seen in operation those mysterious critical processes which create original ideas from memory and imagination. Nevertheless, in recent years scientists, using electronic computers as models, have begun to speculate on what might be the physiology of imagination and the neural counterpart of creative thought.

A brain which is about to give birth to an idea must contain a storage system well supplied with information related to its task. According to one theory these memories are represented in the brain by specific patterns of nerve cell activity—"cell-assemblies"—which go into operation upon receiving an appropriate signal, such as the posing of a problem which demands solution. A well-stocked brain would contain among its ten billion cortical cells enormous numbers of complex, enduring patterns which are ready to weave and intertwine in new and original designs. An unresolved problem, according to this hypothesis, may then be represented by a conflict between specific patterns or by a nagging wave of impulses which continues to circulate through the brain demanding attention. From this unsettled state of affairs a new pathway branches forth, and should it prove successful in stabilizing the once restless circuits, it is possible that the event is judged so important to the cortex that the pattern now rises to the level of conscious attention and is welcomed there as a "new idea." As equilibrium is restored to our neural pathways, as peace and satisfaction temporarily settle upon the agitated circuits, we experience the familiar feeling of joy and the release of tension which accompany the completion of an unfinished task, whether it be the recall of a forgotten name, the solution of a problem, or the creation of a work of art.

If we consider the billions of patterns available to the brain, it is obvious that to avoid chaos there must be some sort of critical control directing the choice of patterns and the sequence in which they are used. So far we have no idea of what this sensitive "cerebral programmer" may be or how it operates. It is without doubt the most baffling and complex mystery of the brain and the aspect which no electronic computer can imitate. Imagination, the ability to conceive possibilities and relationships without first experiencing them,

is one of man's most priceless gifts. It is the chief in-
gredient not only of his artistic creations but of his
ability to reason. To be effective, imagination cannot
be totally random and aimless. It requires direction,
both conscious and unconscious, and must be related
to the problem at hand. It might be an ingenious idea
to employ a flock of grazing sheep as four-legged lawn
mowers, but the idea that a pack of hungry wolves
might be used to munch a lawn into condition must
be rejected as unrealistic, since, among other things,
the nature of the wolf's appetite is such that he might
well solve the problem of man versus grass by eliminating the wrong end. In a more sophisticated sense, the
poet creates his poems from images and ideas supplied
by his fertile imagination. Although he may not know
how he does it, he must bring discipline and control to
his art if a private poetic vision is to be captured in
words and shared with others.

Organizing the raw material of thought is, however,
an extremely delicate task calling for the most subtle
cerebral discretion. Too rigid a cerebral programmer
would have kept Newton from associating the force of
a falling apple with the force of other moving bodies;
too heavy a hand on the helm often replaces the flexible, bold imagination of childhood with the dull,
stereotyped processions of thought which clog the
cerebral highways of many adults.

In what kind of cerebral soil do creative thoughts
and ideas flourish best? Again we can only speculate.
Certainly the superior brain cannot be a lazy brain.

We might expect the nerve cells of the exceptional brain to be unusually active and their synaptic thresholds to be exceptionally inclined to permit circuits to combine and recombine, always experimenting with original and untried routes. Over these lively circuits there must preside that essential critical control which admits relevant even if unconventional patterns, which efficiently rejects the useless, and which provides behavior with focus and direction.

Why one brain possesses these qualities to a greater extent than another is still unknown. One thing may be concluded: The superior human brain differs not so much in the number of its units as in the way it uses its cells. In part, the condition of our nerve cells is already determined at birth, and it is undoubtedly for this reason that no amount of practice or motivation can produce a Mozart or an Einstein. However, much of the ability of our nerve cells to perform is acquired after birth, as experience and education gradually complete the task of engraving and wiring the nervous system. It has been suggested that most people do not use more than half the resources of their brains. Then the important question each of us must ask is: Shall we—who ordinarily demand full value from our other possessions—permit the most marvelous and potentially noble instrument in the world to function undervalued and ill-used, at low speed and on half-power, or shall we exact a fitting "brain's worth" from our unique and priceless human brain?

11

GRUNTS, GROANS, AND HUMAN SPEECH

Left Brain and Right Hand

Subhuman man has been described as a poor, witless, nasty brute whose brain was only a little larger than an ape's brain, whose body had not been fully redesigned for ground life, and who lacked clothes, a house, fire, accumulated knowledge, and language. When and how the brain and body of Homo sapiens evolved from brute man remains a missing chapter in man's history, but by the time the first true men appeared on earth they already possessed a brain rich in reserves of nerve cells and privileged in the possession of speech centers.

Speech is a highly complex function ordinarily requiring muscles, vocal organs, and visual and auditory sensations. Above all, whether we are speaking or listening, writing or reading, human language depends on man's ability to recognize and interpret symbols—in this case, words and numbers. Traditionally it has been taught that in the left cerebral hemisphere of right-handed individuals there are four areas concerned with language functions. These regions are also connected to the thalamus and to the corresponding areas in the right cerebral hemisphere. Even with a microscope no one has been able to distinguish the so-called speech centers from the rest of the cortex, and today there is much difference of opinion concerning these areas and their functions.

There are four areas: one in the third frontal convolution (Broca's convolution) for motor speech; one in the temporal lobe supposedly for storing auditory memory images of words; one in the second frontal convolution for writing; one in the parietal lobe for the visual images of words. The region between the auditory and visual centers is also believed to be concerned with language. It should be stressed, however, that there is considerable disagreement regarding the localization of writing and the visual images of words.

Since our knowledge of speech depends largely on the study of speech disturbances, it is important to consider some of these ailments. Speech disorders may be extremely complicated, for they involve the obvious speech equipment as well as those mysterious mental functions, memory and thought, which cannot be localized but which are represented by speech. In speech defects such as loss of voice, the failure may be due to disease of the voice box (larynx). A variety of speech defects such as stuttering and stammering are caused by disorders of the muscles of articulation. Neither mental function nor the memory and comprehension of words is impaired. In delirium, speech may be deranged as a result of failure at the top level of consciousness. The speech disorders which are of most interest to us here are those listed under the general heading of *aphasia*. In aphasia, speech is impaired not as the result of a muscular paralysis, failure of the eyes and ears to do their part, or even a general loss of reason. Speech impairment is due specifically to a defect in the high-level cortical mechanism which makes it possible for us to understand and use symbols. Rarely pure in form, the many varieties of aphasia, like the disputed speech centers, are difficult to classify. A few examples of aphasia are given here.

The patient may lose the ability to understand the spoken word. As though he were listening to a foreign language, he hears the word clearly enough but does not know what it means. In the same way the memory of written words may be lost. Even though his vision is not affected, such a patient may no longer be able to understand written words. In another defect, motor aphasia, the victim may be unable to express himself in spoken or written language even though the muscles of speech and of the hand are not paralyzed. Such patients may still be able to read and understand spoken language, indicating that their inner language functions are not impaired. In another form of aphasia a patient may use words which have no relation to what he wants to say—for example, saying "up" when he means "down," "June" when he means "January"— or his power to use phrases and sentences may be lost.

It is interesting that as language skills develop in

the little child, he also acquires a preference for using one hand, usually the right, for performing skilled tasks. Although it is less obvious, one foot and one eye also become dominant. Since the right hand is controlled by the left side of the brain, it is significant that it is the left cerebral hemisphere which in right-handed people regulates the important speech functions, and which is usually a little larger. In left-handed individuals, who form about 5 to 10 per cent of the population, the reverse is true: The right hemisphere of the brain is dominant and contains the speech areas. We still do not know enough about the relationship between handedness and speech, but it has been suggested by anthropologists that gestures and the utterance of simple sounds may have been the first form of speech used by primitive man. Eventually these movements and sounds began to be understood as the symbols of the things they represented and finally as the attributes of those things.

Tools of Thought

Even more than the taming of fire, the invention of human speech was man's greatest discovery. It is to his ability to use words—nouns, verbs, and other parts of speech—that man owes his supremacy over all the birds and beasts of his planet and his ability to influence the course of his own evolution. With his dexterous hands he constructed tools to master his environment; with his enlarged brain he created language. Words, as the tools of thought, expanded his memory, increased his reasoning power, and endowed him with the great gift of human imagination. Internal or "silent" speech made it possible for him to handle abstract ideas and to know his own thoughts. Spoken and, later, written speech enabled man to store information and communicate it to others. Since he was able to profit by experience—both his own and that of his fellow man—progress now became possible. No matter how brilliant a young gorilla may be, in all but the basic lessons taught him by his mother he must start over from the beginning of gorilla knowledge, and when he dies all that he has learned goes with him. Thus with the emergence of the thinking, speaking human being, the era of animal dominance on this earth was ended. Intelligent, worried, ambitious, and equipped with the priceless tool of language, man, born naked and helpless, stalked the earth erect and prepared to master it with his own wits.

The use of *semantic* or *articulate* language, as it is called, helped man to escape from the narrow biological world of the animal. It is quite possible for animals and human beings to think without using words. Although we can only guess what an animal's experience is like, it is probable that the hungry dog has a mental image of the meat he would like to eat. In this sense he is "thinking" about the piece of meat. But he does not have a word for *meat*, for *water*, and for the general category *food*. Man does not require words to decide the order of dressing himself, and should he discover that his house is on fire he does not need language to understand what has happened and what he must do immediately. Ordinarily a series of mental pictures is sufficient for this purpose.

Thinking without the aid of verbal symbols, however, is limited to fairly simple matters. As far as we can tell, an animal's thoughts are largely confined to satisfying his immediate needs, and generally the actual need must be present before the animal will act. An ape will make a tool to help him obtain food, an accomplishment which requires both reasoning and imagination, but he will not design one for a future need, experiment with an improved model, or teach another ape, not at the moment hungry, how to make one.

We need words in order to deal with abstract ideas —ideas such as *happiness* and *history*, which, unlike such words as "boy" and "house," represent entities that cannot be touched. It is quite possible to act out emotions such as anger and pleasure without using words, and the general meaning of a raised fist is understood by ape and man as well. But without language it is impossible to communicate such abstract concepts as *black, goodness, justice,* or *science*. It is even difficult to talk about *boy* or *house* in their absence, and without specific words to summon them, "out of sight" is truly "out of mind."

Compared to man's behavior, the activities of an

animal are severely disjointed. Driven by moods and by immediate biological needs, the dog operates fitfully, now tracking food, now an interesting scent, suddenly dropping everything to chase a cat or an automobile. Because man can express his desires in words and in this way preserve them, examine them, and explain them to himself and to others, man can know his own goals and pursue them despite the discouragements of fatigue, poverty, fear, or the distractions of love, loss, and the lapse of time. More consistent than any other animal in his voluntary behavior, man perseveres. It is true that the beaver persists in building a dam and the bird its nest, but this behavior is dictated by instinct and is inherited as an automatic pattern by all beavers and birds alike.

With the acquisition of language and with it the expansion of memory and imagination, the dimensions of primitive man's world widened beyond the urgent needs of the present to include the distant past and the future. This exciting, mysterious world was a place of dreams and superstitions, a private world of himself, and a complex social world of the group to which he belonged. Here he discovered beauty in nature and the spiritual side of his own being, and finally he knew his world to be a place which might exist even without him.

Unfortunately those very words by which man justifies and elaborates his desires often lead into foolish and evil ways known to no animal. Most animals kill only to satisfy natural needs. It has been justly pointed out that man is the only animal that makes war on the members of its own species in the *name* of ideals such as justice and patriotism, or in defense of political and economic philosophies. The ape or lion will fight ferociously to defend his property rights, but his territory must be immediately in danger of attack. On the other hand, one needs words to convince people who live half a world away to fight for a territory they cannot see and with which they are not directly concerned. Only through language can a man be convinced to leave his home and family in order to defend, not the mountains, plains, and waterways of his country, but the principles for which that country stands.

The purpose of language is to communicate feelings, facts, and ideas to ourselves and to others. It is quite possible, however, to use language and yet fail to communicate. We do not receive the intended communication when we listen to the ramblings of the mentally ill, when we are addressed in an unfamiliar language, or when in our own language someone says one thing but means another. For any language, animal or human, to succeed in delivering its message, it is necessary that both the sender and receiver share a similar understanding of the sound, gesture, or symbol used. To the extent that you and I attach the same meaning to the word "black," we understand each other; as long as a husband understands the mute language of his wife's eyes, the dog the intent of another dog's growl, the student the meaning of "excellence," language, both *emotional* and *semantic*, has succeeded in its purpose of communicating.

What actually is the difference between semantic and emotional speech? No one would deny that animals communicate with one another vocally as well as with gestures, just as the human mother learns to interpret the different cries and gurgles of her baby. Emotional language communicates mood, general physiological state, and such basic feelings as anger, fear, pleasure, and pain, but it cannot name and describe specific objects or ideas. Although animals use expressions which are equivalent in human language to "wow!," "O.K.," and "watch out!" such language is vague and extremely limited in the amount of detail it can convey. Man, too, leans heavily on emotional language, particularly within the circle of his immediate family and intimate friends where sighs and grunts, gestures and raised eyebrows communicate valuable messages to those who hold the key to their meaning.

Unlike emotional speech, semantic speech conveys specific information by means of symbols, usually words, which stand only for the things they represent. Emotional speech, the first language of the human baby, does not depend on the cerebral hemispheres; semantic speech does. Only as the babbling infant's nervous system matures do the muscles of speech learn to obey his will, and only as the paths in his cerebral cortex begin to multiply and branch does he develop the ability to think and communicate in symbols.

Great effort has been exerted to teach apes to talk, but as yet no one has succeeded. We are not born knowing how to speak, and the symbolic system of any language must be taught to the child by the society in which he lives; otherwise he remains little more than an animal. However, the ability to learn to speak is part of man's birthright. Human voice organs are superior to those of any animal, but most of all speech is the gift of the brain—of the speech areas which control the muscles of speech and of the great cortical association areas which enable man to remember the meanings of words, numbers, or other devices, and to arrange these symbols to represent his thoughts. Apes and higher animals can use symbols, and they are frequently trained to understand the meanings of words in our language, but from what we can tell, animals do not ordinarily think in symbols. Only man and possibly the dolphin have a sufficient number of brain pathways to contain the countless associations by which symbols are linked with the things they represent. They are probably the only creatures that regularly use symbols for most of their thinking.

At this point we must mention briefly the recent studies of the language of the dolphins, those highly intelligent members of the whale family. The amiable dolphin converses in an extremely complicated language of high frequency whistles, squeaks, grunts, and buzzes which apparently can be combined to produce a large vocabulary. Unlike the ape, the dolphin can imitate human language in a voice which, although in the style of Donald Duck, is nevertheless quite intelligible. Considering the large amount of cortical territory needed to maintain a system of symbolic communication, it is not surprising that the dolphin has a brain which easily rivals our own in the number of its cells. Actually, the dolphin brain is larger than ours and in a given area it contains as many cells as the human cerebral cortex.

We hope one day to be able to communicate with the dolphin, who is possibly the most intelligent of all animals, and scientists are working hard to decipher dolphin language. It is not an easy matter, however, for the dolphin inhabits a world so different from ours that, beyond those basic needs shared by all living creatures, it is difficult for human beings to imagine what it is that one dolphin would tell another or the nature of a dolphin's intellectual life.

The Trouble with Words

Long ago, before the era of science, in the days of magic and witchcraft—and even today among primitive people and the superstitious members of our own supposedly advanced society—words, woven into magic incantations, were considered to possess supernatural powers. Today we know that the wizardry of words lies not in the words themselves but in the way they influence the thoughts and ideas of those who use them.

The secret to the magic power of words, be it good or evil, derives from the fact that a symbol only *stands for* an object or an idea: It is not the thing itself. The warning cry of an animal is a signal; a smile or a moan is a sign. Sign and signal are still charged with the emotion of the moment. On the other hand, symbols such as the words "cry" and "smile" are no longer inhabited by a living emotion and can be understood only by those who know what feelings they are supposed to represent. Anything can be a symbol providing the people using it agree to attach the same meaning to the token. Thus "knife," "Messer," and "couteau" all mean knife to those who possess the key to the symbol system. A dollar bill, actually no more than a lifeless piece of paper, is a most expressive and powerful symbol as long as the people who use it continue to agree on its meaning.

The advantages of a thinking system based on symbols are tremendous. We manipulate numbers, add and subtract, multiply and divide, without going through the laborious process of counting all the items involved in each operation. Converted into verbal and written symbols, information is more easily stored and may be recalled at a time when the original stimulus is no longer present. We do not have to see a table to deal with it mentally. The word "table" stands for all the properties and functions we observe in that article of furniture, and once it is tagged with a name we know without studying a table what it has in common with other objects like it. Words therefore shorten and streamline the learning process. Many of our symbols are extremely complex. The word "courage" is a convenient term for a considerable number of subtle and vague concepts. Communication would quickly grind to a halt if each time we wished to use an idea we had to list everything we meant by it, and yet, ironically, we often get lost in a verbal jungle because neither sender nor receiver fully understands what is meant by highly abstract words.

Here, in the fact that words are not containers which hold pure meaning, lies their potential power to deceive. The electrical impulses which correspond to the sound or sight of a word and those stored in the brain as its meaning are not the same. Thus from "Ma-ma" to Einstein's equation "$E=mc^2$," words must ever flow through the brain seeking their meanings. There are many different ways of speaking the word "water": We may whisper it, shout it, or pronounce it with a drawl or a foreign accent. Low-pitched sounds go to one part of the brain and high-pitched sounds to an adjacent area. The electrical patterns which correspond to the various ways of writing the word "water" are still different. Yet all of these patterns must in some way arouse a single set of pathways in the brain which correspond to the meaning, in English, of that specific chemical compound known as "water."

In some unknown way the brain finds the electrical pattern which is common to all of them. "It is as though," explained a distinguished scientist, "the meaning of a word were locked up in a cupboard which had to be opened by a key." There may be many keys to the lock, but they must all possess the secret design which corresponds to the pattern of the lock. Only then are word and meaning united.

The problem is still more complicated, for no word has one single "correct" meaning. There are at least two different kinds of meaning for every word. First, a word names something—an object, a person, an event, an action, or an idea. Second, a word refers to one's private experience—one's associations—with it. We need not be conscious of these associations, but our understanding of a word is influenced by the culture in which we live, by our education, and by our personal experience.

In the first sense, the word "John" designates a specific person, but in making it possible to think about him, your past experience with John will color your thoughts. Immediately the meaning of "John" becomes *what "John" means to you*. Into each little word is packed a fragment of our personal story. Nothing more than a modest combination of sounds or a few dashes and wiggles on paper, every word is an ambassador from the brain, the representative of experiences and information scattered throughout the molecular hiding places in our nerve cells.

In its vocabulary and grammatical structure language mirrors the attitudes of the culture to which it belongs.

"Snow" has a somewhat different meaning to the Eskimo and to the residents of Florida. The Eskimo has many more words to designate the different forms of what most Americans and Europeans simply call "snow," and he uses different words for wind-blown snow, hard-packed snow, and snow on the ground. Despite this, "snow" means pretty much the same thing to most people. Unfortunately the meanings of abstract words such as "honesty," "nature," and "patriotism" are not universally agreed upon. The word "beauty," although employed freely in our conversation, conveys different information to the many people who use it. The Ubangi tribesman has one concept of feminine beauty, the American man quite another, and even within the same culture one man's pretty girl may be Plain Jane to another. It requires more than a dictionary and a knowledge of grammar to bridge the gap in understanding between the people who speak the many different human languages of this earth.

At the same time that the values of our culture are reflected in our language, words and the patterns in which they are used influence the way in which we think and color our perception of the world. There is no way of saying "I kill him" in Greenlandic because the language has no transitive (action) verbs. One must say instead, "He dies to me," which lacks the action and violence of the first expression. Most of us are unaware of the extent to which we are victims of the thought habits imposed on us by speech.

We use words and numbers to save ourselves the trouble of thinking about the objects and ideas they represent. The danger of entrusting our thoughts to a set of conventional symbols is that like the woolly mammoth buried in a block of ice, our thoughts may eventually be frozen in the words which embody them. Too often clichés and trite expressions take the place of thinking, or we shuffle symbols to obtain desired ends without checking the clarity of the thinking behind the screen of the words or the truth of the conclusions obtained by such verbal sleight of hand.

Few people inspect the meaning of the word "communism," yet in its name all sorts of deeds have been done and events justified. The words "nature" and "society" are ambiguous packages used freely and carelessly to mean any number of uncertain things. Although it is an exciting experience to watch a little child learn to speak, at the same time we regret the ease with which his delightful imagination and his need to discover his own definitions are finally shackled and smothered by the arbitrary demands of the language he is learning. No longer is his lambchop bone a rocking chair and his chair a galloping horse. He learns, rightly so, the true functions of these objects. In time he will also be able to say, "It is snowing" without bothering to go outside to see what snow really looks like. The price we pay for such progress is often too costly, for to be enriched by language it is not necessary that we be dominated by it. Occasionally we must rediscover the soundless beauty of falling snow and the kinship of snow to water; the still-hidden properties of atoms and even of lambchop bones may be discovered by those who are unwilling to take the rigid grooves of language for granted.

Whether language is to serve as the link between man and his fellow man, between the individual and himself, whether as the tool of thought it is to bring him greater freedom, or whether he is to become the prisoner of his own invention is up to man. The scientist must constantly check to be certain that the symbols he uses—numbers and words—represent physical reality. The poet knows well the magical power of language to dissolve the conventional, the ordinary view of the world, and each of us must watch over the language to which we entrust our thoughts—thoughts by which man ultimately produces his greatest glories or most pitiful follies.

12

DO COMPUTERS THINK?

The second half of the twentieth century has been called the Atomic Age, or described romantically as the Jet or Space Age. In practical terms, however, this is the Electronic Age, and the unsung hero of our times is the extremely small, negatively charged electron which revolves at incredible speeds around the nucleus of the atom. The electron has never been seen, is almost weightless, and yet is the indispensable servant of our era. Without such electronic devices as radio, television, and radar, without automatic electronic control systems and the midcentury marvel, the highspeed computer, the exploration of the atom and of space would remain a dream beyond the reach of mankind.

Man has just begun to discover the many uses to which he can put the versatile computer. The machines we have at present handle office paper-work, supervise industrial processes, "dry-run" atomic submarines, forecast the weather, predict business trends, and guide space ships to cosmic destinations. Computers also translate languages, compose music, play chess and checkers; they calculate, compare, decide, predict, and even learn by experience.

Operating at astronomical speeds, an electronic computer can solve a problem faster than 500,000 men using desk calculators. One of the earliest large-scale computers at the Los Alamos Atomic Energy Laboratory solved a problem requiring nine million mathematical operations. The machine, which was a tortoise by today's standards, produced the answer in 150 hours. A mathematician would have required 1500 years to complete the task—certainly a discouraging prospect. The latest machines multiply at an average rate of 200,000 to 500,000 numbers containing 36 pieces of information in a second, and even these dazzling speed records are destined to be surpassed.

So talented are these machines and so dramatically have they affected our lives that they have been dubbed "Giant Brains" or "Thinking Machines" and are regarded by those who do not know how they work with a mixture of awe and distrust. If a machine can outperform, even outwit its designer, if it can plan and produce its descendents, it is natural to wonder if, indeed, as in some frightening science-fiction story, man may one day become the slave of his creation. Before we consider the question of whether a computer can think, we must first dispel the aura of mystery and magic which too often surrounds and obscures the machine: We must understand what a computer is and how it operates. Finally, it is necessary to explain what we mean by "thinking."

Extensions of Man

The computer is a tool—admittedly a member of an elite class of tools—but in purpose and principle no different from any of the devices man has invented to extend his own physical abilities. To improve upon his arm and hand, man created tools such as the shovel and drill. Eventually he replaced the muscle power which drove these hand implements with nonliving sources of power such as water and electricity; the shovel became a steam shovel, the drill a power drill.

Just as man has built automobiles, telephones, and microscopes as specialized improvements of his legs, ears, and eyes, so too he has created the computer to serve his thought processes—to give speed and accuracy to his calculations and to rescue him from the deadening drudgery of repetitive paper work. The ancestor of all computing machines was the human hand, for it was on his ten fingers that man first counted. Later he counted with beads, and the ancient Chinese invented the abacus, a calculating tool still used in many parts of the world. In the seventeenth century young Blaise Pascal, the great French mathematician, built a crude, gear-driven adding machine which counted numbers and kept track of them on a series of notched wheels. In the useful desk calculator man has substituted electricity for the muscle power which formerly drove hand-operated calculating machines, and today, vacuum tubes and transistors have given wings to computation, making it possible to count at electronic speeds.

Both the steam shovel and the desk calculator must be guided step by step by their human operators. More advanced tools are those with the power to regulate themselves—to determine the next move, to make decisions, to discover their own mistakes, and even to decide when a task is completed. Behind the automatic or self-regulating machine there is still a human brain, but it is now one step removed. Because the human operator can no longer be seen in the "driver's seat" when a computer launches a rocket or a washing machine "decides" to shut itself off because it is overloaded is no reason to doubt the operator's existence.

Self-regulating devices are so common that we take them for granted. The thermostat in your home is a simple example of a tool which controls itself. Ordered to maintain room temperature at a certain level, the thermostat receives information concerning the temperature in the room and obediently turns the heating system on or off whenever the temperature exceeds the given level or drops below it. Naturally, in order to regulate itself the machine must know the results of its own behavior, and like living organisms from worms to human beings, it requires a "nervous system" containing feedback circuits.

The automatic elevator and the automatic washing

machine are accepted today as the rather ordinary tools of our age; we would hardly call them "brains." Yet they are simple examples of machines which process information, the same in principle as the most complicated and dazzling electronic computer. Equipped with the necessary feedback mechanisms and a primitive memory, the self-service elevator receives and remembers requests for floors, signals its location, decides when to move up or down, refuses to move if its door is not closed, knows when an assignment has been completed, and ignores the requests of impatient riders who try to browbeat the elevator by jabbing the call button or holding it down.

Automatic elevators, however, and most computers, no matter how flexible and intricate, always perform according to standards and instructions built into them ahead of time by their human masters. From drawing board to scrap pile the lessons of experience are wasted on most machines; they never mature. This is not true of the human brain, which learns, profits from experience, and corrects its own mistakes. Recently man, ingenious and undaunted by technical problems, has created a highly gifted species of machines, ranging from electronic mice to complex game-playing computers, capable of learning and improving their performance as they operate.

Once provided with the rules of the game, it is a simple matter for a computer to play checkers. First the computer surveys the consequences, several moves ahead, of all the possible moves it might make, and then it calculates the best course of action. Such a machine, of course, will always play the same kind of game, making its moves according to pre-established rules set for it by its programmer. The next step is to write a program making it possible for the computer to learn from its playing experience and to improve its game—even to the point of defeating its designer. To do this the machine stores all the moves it makes in its memory. Then, having played a sufficient number of games according to its original instructions, the computer begins to rewrite these directions. It evaluates those moves and tactical situations on the board which in actual competition proved successful and in future games relies on them, discarding the strategy which did not lead to victory. The future of learning machines, of which the checker-playing machine is but one illustration, is extremely exciting, for these are the machines which most resemble the living brain.

Since brain rather than brawn increasingly determines how man is to meet his needs, it is fitting that his tools should also evolve from extensions of his body to extensions of his brain. We need not be embarrassed because a computer can add numbers faster than we can, any more than we are ashamed of ourselves because we let airplanes do our flying.

On-Off Mathematicians

For all the glamor and hocus-pocus surrounding the "wonder child" of the twentieth century, and despite the extraordinary complexity of highspeed computer systems, it is sobering to realize that a computer does nothing a human being cannot do with pencil and paper—providing he has the time. Furthermore, the computer accomplishes all its marvels by performing the basically simple operations of arithmetic: addition, subtraction, multiplication, and division. Because letters of the alphabet, and therefore words, may be represented by numbers, the computer can also handle those nonmathematical problems for which there is a logical solution. It does this by making the simple logical decisions of *yes* and *no*, to which even the most complex logical operations may eventually be reduced.

If a machine is to solve equations and make logical decisions, it must first be taught the rules of arithmetic and logic, Fortunately this is not as difficult as it might at first seem, for the tubes, switches, and magnetic materials of electronic hardware are capable of existing in only one of two possible states: on or off, conducting current or not, magnetized in one direction or in the opposite. Even the familiar paper punched card is, at a specific location, either punched or not punched. This two-state condition of vital computer parts lends itself most naturally to expressing the concepts of *yes* and *no*, and it is for this reason that electronic circuits can be taught to solve logical problems.

Typical computers, with their two-state components, their yes-no logic, are unable to use the ordinary decimal system—a ten-state system—to which we are accustomed. This is not a serious problem. It is only because we have ten fingers that we developed a number system based on groups of ten and requiring ten digits, 0 to 9, to express the smaller units within the group. There are other counting systems, however, based on groups of five, twelve, twenty; the ancient Babylonians used sixty. Computers use a *binary* system of counting based on groups of two, thus requiring only two numbers, 0 and 1, to express the group units.

This is how the binary scale operates. In the familiar decimal system every time we move a digit one place to the left, we multiply the number by ten: 1, 10, 100, 1000 and so forth. Thus the decimal number 7394 means seven thousands, three hundreds, nine tens and four ones. In the binary system each move of the digit to the left multiplies the number by two: 1, 2, 4, 8, 16, 32, and so forth. The binary number for the decimal value, 13, is written 1101 and reads from left to right: one eight, one four, no twos and one one. The number 110 in the binary scale does not mean one hundred and ten; it means six. (See the chart in Fig. 24 for a further comparison of binary and decimal scales.) Although the binary system may appear unwieldy to us at first, this simple two digit scale is ideal for the electronic computer whose components exist in only an ON or OFF state, or an electronic equivalent of this condition. Thus ON represents the number one, and OFF stands

DECIMAL VALUE	PLACE VALUE				
	16	8	4	2	1
0	0	0	0	0	0
1	0	0	0	0	1
2	0	0	0	1	0
3	0	0	0	1	1
4	0	0	1	0	0
5	0	0	1	0	1
6	0	0	1	1	0
7	0	0	1	1	1
8	0	1	0	0	0
9	0	1	0	0	1
10	0	1	0	1	0
11	0	1	0	1	1
12	0	1	1	0	0
13	0	1	1	0	1
14	0	1	1	1	0
15	0	1	1	1	1
16	1	0	0	0	0

Fig. 24 *Comparison of decimal and binary scales*

for zero. The binary digit 1101 would appear: ON ON OFF ON.

Two Families

There are two major types of computers—*analogue* and *digital*. The analogue computer uses a physical property, such as the length between two points on a slide rule, the rotation of a gear, or the strength of an electrical current, to imitate the components of problems which may themselves not be easily accessible. The *physical* properties of the substitute system are used to represent the numbers in an equation: They behave "analogously" to the equation or problem. The clock, the slide rule, and the automobile speedometer are simple examples of analogue computers. We can measure time, which is determined by the rotation of the earth, by observing the movement of the stars across the sky, but for most of us this is impractical. Instead we use a handy little computer called a clock, in which a pointer moving around a dial corresponds to the turning of the earth on its axis. In the speedometer the rate of turning of a cylindrical shaft is converted into a numerical approximation of speed in miles per hour. Analogue computers are used to solve differential equations and play an important role in simulating the performance of missile and rocket systems.

Digital computers are counters and receive their name from the fingers, or digits, on which primitive man first counted the number of animals he had killed, the number of weapons he possessed, or the members of his family. Like the abacus or the desk calculator, the computer performs the elementary operations of arithmetic, but because the basic unit in the modern electronic computer is at least 100,000 times faster in action than the living nerve cell, the machine can compute at fantastic speeds. Speed, accuracy, and endurance—not intelligence—are the great virtues of the computer. Since most machines cannot accept information in its ordinary form, facts, figures, statements, and instructions must first be predigested and converted to a numerical code which the machine can understand. The computer must then be spoon-fed with detailed operating instructions telling it step by step what to do with the data supplied to it and where to locate information in its storage system.

Knitting, embroidery, building model airplanes, and constructing hi-fi equipment from special kits are examples of processes in which you produce intricate designs or complicated products by repeating a few basically simple operations according to a set of instructions which supply the number, sequence, or location of these steps. In solving a mathematical problem it is not always possible to predict at the outset the entire sequence of steps. To provide for this complication the machine must be given special instructions so that after inspecting the results of an intermediate operation it can decide which of several possible steps is appropriate as its next move.

If A, B, C, and D stand for four different numbers, a simple operating instruction might tell a computer:

1. Take A from storage location 121. Take B from storage location 129. Find $A + B$. Store the result.

2. Take C from storage location 209. Take D from storage location 326. Find $C \times D$. Store the result.

3. Now take the results of steps 1 and 2 out of storage and compare them. If the result of step 1 is a number larger than that of step 2, divide the result of 1 by the result of 2 and print the answer. *But* if the result of step 1 is a number smaller than that of 2, consult storage location 456 for additional instructions.

Giant electronic computers—data-processing machines, as they are called—actually consist of several machine systems combined in one unit. Information recorded on devices such as punched cards and magnetic tape or printed in magnetic ink is fed into the machine through the INPUT system, while the answer to the problem is released in the OUTPUT system. The final or intermediate results of the computer's work may appear as typewritten information, as indications on a dial, or they may once again be recorded on punched cards or on tape. The STORAGE unit is an electronic filing cabinet in which information recorded on magnetic tape, magnetic discs or in tiny magnetic rings, called *cores*, is completely indexed and readily accessible to the computer. The stored information may consist of original data memorized by the system, intermediate results, reference tables, or special operating instructions. The PROCESSING division is the central system of the computer. It consists of an *arithmetic* unit which does the actual work of calculation and a *control* section which, having access to the information and instructions held in storage, provides the calculator with the rules of arithmetic and logic and coordinates the performance of the entire machine. It is the control unit which has won the computer its reputation for intelligence.

Robots

To physiologists and psychologists the most interesting class of computers is not the giant data processing system, specifically created to relieve man of tedious calculating chores or to rescue him from stifling in his own paperwork, but the experimental family of electro-mechanical models designed to mimic the drives, emotions, learning processes, and even the social behavior of living creatures.

Since man built the robot, he has the advantage of knowing what he put into it and how it works. Engineers have long known the value of using a model of a system as a practical method of studying the original system—the principle employed in the analogue computer. Today the easily dissected robot plays an important role in the physiologist's laboratory. The study of electronic nervous systems often suggests the possibility of parallel mechanisms in living creatures, while an understanding of the robot's limitations helps scientists and philosophers to define the differences between machines and living organisms.

One such little device, named *Machina speculatrix* by its designer, Dr. W. Grey Walter, looks like a large turtle and has a "two-cell" nervous system, consisting of two tubes, two relays, two condensers, two electric motors, and two batteries. The robot's "sense receptors" are a photoelectric cell which makes it sensitive to light and an electrical contact which provides *Speculatrix* with a sense of touch. Even with such simple equipment the machine's behavior, like that of a living animal, is flexible and unpredictable.

The machine is designed so that it is attracted to a moderate light. In going toward this light *Speculatrix* will pause first to deal with an obstacle blocking its way, such as a steep slope or another robot, and then with admirable persistence will resume the pursuit of its goal. Carefully exploring the ground, in a remarkable imitation of a living animal, the robot looks around for problems to solve, makes decisions, competes with others to reach a common goal such as a light, finds its way home, and remains there long enough to recharge its batteries—the robot counterpart of dinner.

The descendants of this machine have many other talents. One model, which has been provided with a conditioned reflex circuit, is capable of learning from experience certain facts of robot life not originally built into the circuits with which it was "born." At one point in the course of the creature's education, a conflict was established in its circuits by teaching it to *come at the sound of a whistle* and to *halt at the sound of a whistle*. Having been taught both to "go to sound" and to "halt to sound," the robot found itself in a pitiful dilemma. Unable to act, unwilling to return to its home in time to have its batteries recharged, con fused and helpless, the electronic toy suffered the mechanical equivalent of a nervous breakdown. Neither to be mocked nor feared, mechanical animals, like living animals, are the laboratory tools man uses in the unending search to understand himself.

Giant Brain or Giant Moron?

In a remarkably short time man has built calculating wizards, talented computers which learn and mature, and strange little battery-operated animals whose performance, were we not aware of their electronic anatomy, would be difficult to distinguish from the behavior of simple living animals. Standing just across the threshold of the atomic age, man contemplates the gifted electronic infants he has created and wonders somewhat uncomfortably in what way his intelligent tools and gadgets differ from himself. Is it possible that in an electronic thinking machine he has built a "brain" which one day may be superior to his own? Or—and it seems an even sadder thought—is his own brain nothing more than an intricately wired machine, highly versatile, but slow in operation and prone to error?

"A living organism can reproduce itself; a machine cannot," man reminds himself, taking comfort for a moment in his biological superiority. To this claim the computer designer replies that computers are already helping to design their replacements and theoretically there is no reason why a computer should not direct the entire process of manufacturing its colleagues, its assistants, and its successors.

"Computers lack feelings," the argument continues, arriving on difficult but safer ground. Although engineers assure us that it is a simple matter to build feelings into a computer and to simulate everything from glee to insanity, the physiologist points to the difference between emotional display and inner feeling and therefore disagrees. Remembering the hissing, clawing cats in the sham rage experiments and considering ourselves when, in spite of sorrow, we smile and maintain a brave front, we must admit that the computer designer has done nothing more than provide a machine with outward behavior which in his opinion appears to express an inner emotional state. We do not know what a "happy" computer feels, if indeed it feels anything, and we have no right to assume that a machine feels frightened just because it halts when kicked or because it runs away from us.

Machines learn, remember, and solve logical problems, but do they think? If we consider the important role of biological drives, of motivation, and of emotions such as love and hate in coloring and focusing our thoughts, we should not reduce thinking to the dry, mechanical process of deductive reasoning, depriving thought of its inspiration, direction, and drive. Then even in a restricted sense, does the computer think?

One way of answering this question is to say that the computer produces thoughts, but it does not think

—anymore than the paper rolls which produce music in the old-fashioned player piano can be said, in anything but the mechanical sense, to be "playing the piano." Following the predictable rules of deductive logic, the computer makes comparisons, decisions, and solves problems. Its output is often more accurate and its logic more reliable than that of many a living "thinking machine." But unless we wish to degrade the meaning of even routine, noncreative thinking, we must recognize that the machine's "intelligence" is artificial; it is man who thinks for the computer. Just as the keys on the mechanical piano follow orders, the computer does only what it is told—it thinks by proxy. Without man to plug it in, to provide it with problems, and to tell it how to solve them, the machine is a useless collection of metal and glass, tubes and wires. Even computers such as chess-playing and checker-playing machines, which learn from experience and wire their own circuits as they play, are not free of their inventors, for these machines play games, learn, and improve according to a program written for them by their human masters.

It is generally agreed that a computer can be programmed to do anything a man knows how to do. If the "thinking" machine is to be compared to the thinking brain, we must eventually ask: Can a computer be original? Can a machine be creative?

Here, at last, we have cornered the computer since imagination and creativity are considered to be attributes of living creatures which present-day machines cannot imitate. This depends, of course, on what we mean by originality or creativeness. Computers can be programmed to compose music or write television plays. But in such cases man is again thinking for the computer, merely allowing the machine to compute the possible variations of a given set of conditions and rules. The computer which reels off dozens of television plays upon being instructed A *equals gun*, B *equals sheriff*, C *equals horse*, and furthermore that *horse cannot ride sheriff or gun* does nothing a man could not do had he the patience to work out all the possible plot combinations.

The shadow of the man continues to hang over the machine because such a play-writing computer is being "creative" according to the rules and definitions set for it by its operator. The truth is, man does not create his works of art by computation. The laws of original thought—if such there be—remain unknown. Imagination, insight, and intuition, by which art from kindergarten to museum is created and by which scientific discoveries are made, are spontaneous processes which, unlike reason and logic, follow no predictable rules and are heavily in debt to human emotions.

It has been calculated that given enough time it is theoretically possible for a computer, using all possible combinations of the letters of the alphabet and other typographical signs, to produce by chance all the great and small written works man has ever created or ever will create—from marketing lists to the plays of Shakespeare, including the lines Shakespeare himself dis-

carded. Unfortunately, along with the masterpieces
and trivia it would also produce an almost infinite
amount of nonsense, and the problem of sorting the
gems from the gibberish would be a task for an army
of all but immortal editors.

We cannot, however, teach a machine how to write
a masterpiece such as *Hamlet* or Beethoven's *Ninth
Symphony* because we ourselves do not know how it
is done, nor did Shakespeare or Beethoven possess the
secret to the mechanisms of their genius. At the same
time we should not belittle our own brains if someday
a computer composes its own "Ninth Symphony." It
is an unlikely event. Yet should a musical computer
create such a marvel, it would reflect to man's credit,
for it would mean that he had discovered the secret
of creative genius and imparted his knowledge to the
machine. The computer is versatile and it is still a
baby, but man always remains one step ahead of his
tool.

To take comfort in the computer's lack of imagination, to name creativity as the dividing line between
man and machine, is to put the cart before the horse.
It is a difficult criterion to use when attempting to dif-
ferentiate machines from lower animals. The computer's lack of imagination is merely a symptom of its
fundamental limitation—its dependence on man to tell
it what to do and how to do it, and to provide it with
purpose and direction. Whether the computer is filing
bank checks or exploring the surface of the moon, the
goals it pursues and the functions it performs originate

in the brains of its designers and are built into it by human beings. Born of man's needs and created by human imagination and reason, today's computer is a self-regulating tool which serves a purpose and obeys orders which originate elsewhere. It understands neither what it does nor the relevance of its output and will go on calculating even if its house has caught fire and the room in which it works has begun to fill with smoke.

Animals and human beings also pursue goals, and their behavior has meaning and direction. The difference is that the conscious and unconscious purposes of living creatures, although influenced by the environment, originate or are "manufactured" within the individual himself. We do not know what our "cerebral programmer" is or how our thoughts are created, and the physiological source of our drives and ambitions is still baffling. Nor can we be certain of mankind's ultimate purpose—if, indeed, he has one. For man the future is uncertain and uncommitted, filled with opportunity, possibility, and hope.

There is an interesting parallel between the machine and people who are hypnotized or have been brainwashed in that, at least temporarily, the purposes and goals of these individuals are supplied artificially by an outside agent—the hypnotist or brain-washer. So sensitive are we to the similarity between the living and the inanimate automaton that we call such people "tools" or "zombies." We relieve these living robots of the moral and ethical responsibility for their behavior which originates in the freedom ordinarily associated with human beings, but not with animals.

The computer reflects our purposes, it functions with our intelligence and our defects, and on the dials, tapes, and typewriter paper of its output system it represents our goals in all their glory or folly. Until an entirely new family of computers is developed which in some way has freed itself of our purposes, even the most talented computer will remain an inanimate extension of man—a tool.

The Computing Brain

To have set the machine in its place is not to despise it. Just as computer designers have tried to imitate the living brain in building their electronic models, neurophysiologists have welcomed the computer as a valuable laboratory "animal." In many respects the brain is a living computer, remarkably like the machine in its components and operation; in many other ways it is entirely unlike the computer. By forcing us to explore the nature of originality and to define what we mean by thinking; by stressing the problems of accuracy and error, efficiency, and effectiveness; and by insisting that we analyze the differences between the human brain and the brainy machine, the computer has added to our understanding of our own brain.

As in the computer, the route from input to output in the brain depends on a calculation system, a control unit, and a memory division. Like the machine, the brain contains complex electrical networks in which the cell body of the neuron corresponds to the vacuum tube or transistor, while the nerve fiber is a living wire. Inborn reflexes are similar to the computer's built-in circuits, and the synaptic endings of the neuron, like electronic switches, keep circuits closed or open, conducting or not conducting. Depending on the combinations in which switches are opened or closed, impulses in both the nervous system and the computer may be routed along a variety of pathways or kept circulating in a closed circuit.

In the on-off property of its nerve cells, in its yes-no arithmetic, the brain appears to behave very much like a digital computer operating with the binary arithmetic of one and zero. Since the performance of the nerve cell is also affected by physical factors such as its spatial arrangement in the brain, its position in relation to other cells, chemical changes, and such mechanical changes as those caused by muscular contractions, the brain is also believed to operate like an analogue computer. It has been suggested that in the brain, digital and analogue procedures may alternate with each other, resulting in a mixed computing process far more complex than anything we know in a machine.

Isolating and comparing those properties held in common by objects, situations, or ideas are some of the fundamental duties of brainwork. The following examples of the brain's digital behavior, although oversimplified, are useful and intriguing. When you meet someone on the street, your brain quickly refers to its memory files and returns a yes-no decision on whether

that face is known to you. When you look at your fountain pen and your fingers and observe their shape, the
electrical input is routed over the optic nerves to the
brain, which matches these impressions with the electrical pattern of a cylinder already stored in its memory,
thus calculating one of the ways in which fingers and
pens are similar. On a higher level, the finger-pen input
may be compared to the data stored as the concept of
"tool," whereupon a series of yes-no binary computa-
tions feed still another resemblance into the cerebral
output.

Comparing the computing brain to the computing
machine is a fascinating occupation as well as a fertile
source of new theories. It has been found that in building a computer it is more practical to separate the
memory unit from the functional unit (the arithmetic
section). This suggests the possibility that the basic
components of human memory may not be the same as
the functional unit (the nerve cell), but may depend
on a separate physical entity such as the junctions between the cells (synapses). We do not know if the
brain, in performing its calculations, uses the same
technique as the computer—whether the brain's arithmetic and logic units, so similar in their on-off flip-
flops to electronic devices, actually operate as in the
machine.

Closely related to the mystery of cerebral computation is the question of how the brain achieves precision,
of how it avoids error, and if, in fact, "precision" has
the same meaning to the brain and to the digital com-

puter. The sum of two plus two is four—and only four. An approximate answer of five, given by a digital computer, is not only inaccurate, but were the computer to use this figure to perform other equally imprecise calculations, the errors would accumulate to the point where the final result would be complete nonsense. Yet in the brain, where hundreds of thousands of neurons discharge in a single operation, what happens to the level of accuracy if a few neurons misfire or if, by accident, several uninvited neurons join the chorus? Will the streams of impulses triggered by the sight of a mouse add up to a cat instead? One theory states that the calculations of the brain may be statistical rather than arithmetical. This means that it may be the *frequency* of the impulse train rather than the *exact number* of impulses which counts. "Frequency" is a ratio which compares the number of actual impulses to the number of possible impulses. Or it may be the statistical relationship between several trains of impulses arriving on different fibers which is significant—thus not the exact but the relative number of these impulses. The brain might then contain parallel computing systems running along different nerve fibers, so that, to put it crudely, if the majority of impulses are mouse-impulses, the general trend is accepted, it is a mouse we see, and other contributions are ignored.

At *Full Throttle*

The human brain is perhaps a million years old. The modern computer was born less than forty years ago, and today's models are still at the foot of their family tree, the primitive ancestors of generations of computers yet to evolve. Computers of the future will learn to do their own programming from a set of general instructions. There are already experimental models which understand the human voice, and it is predicted that in time the computer will respond to direct questions, even answer by voice, thereby simplifying the laborious, time-consuming task of coding all the machine's instructions. Tomorrow's "giant" data processing systems will be even smaller than television sets and are expected to spread from their present domain in the office and laboratory to the home, where they will perform such tedious tasks as preparing menus and marketing lists, scheduling family appointments, and handling budgets and money. The future of the computer is brilliant, limited only by man's imagination and ingenuity.

The true challenge of the computer lies not in the childish fear that we may have created a Frankenstein or a mechanical genius which will eventually enslave us but in the opportunity to let the brain do work suited to its unique talents. Far from humbling him, the electronic tool should encourage man to devote himself to those concerns for which he is superbly equipped—to the creation of original thought and works of art, to the pursuit of learning and self-knowledge and the acquisition of wisdom.

As the transistor and its electronic relatives take over

the dull, repetitious tasks of human thinking, as man is freed from the increasing drudgery of routine, noncreative thinking, his brain, relieved of mental indigestion, might then operate at the upper levels of its ability. Such a prospect is both pleasing and tremendously exciting and should threaten only those individuals who remain content to waste their valuable brain power on work better performed by a machine. As the muscle power of the wash woman is replaced by the automatic washing machine, so the plodding mental toil—until recently, performed by file clerks and routine bookkeepers—is gradually being taken over by efficient data processing machines which swallow, sort, and digest great masses of information with the dazzling speed of the electron. Human beings, however, will not become obsolete, for now more than ever we shall require men and women to discover and organize the problems computers are to solve and to grapple with problems which previously would not have been considered because of the mass of work involved. We shall always need people to attend to those specifically human matters which are neither a monkey's business nor the province of a machine.

The course of man's evolution is directed by his brain, not by the physical adaptations of his body. Now that human destiny is being charted at increasingly sophisticated mental levels, there will be an even greater premium on brain power. Success in the struggle for survival in a world which has grown no friendlier since the first molecules of life drifting in the primordial slime began to reproduce themselves may well be the reward of those individuals and their descendants who recognize that the brain is much more than a calculating machine and who prepare and encourage their own brains to perform at peak capacity. It is possible that the potential talents of the human brain surpass anything of which we have yet dreamed.

13

WHERE THE FUTURE BEGINS

Nothing, not even the architecture of the universe, endures unchanged. Stars burn out and new ones are born, and billions of years from now our own star, the sun, to which our planet's destiny is linked, will consume itself and blink out. The earth will not survive the death throes of the sun, but will first roast and then freeze, finally whirling on through the eons a dark, frozen waste. Before such cosmic disaster overtakes our planet, man may have packed his belongings and moved to the outskirts of another star.

In the beginning, 4.5 to 5 billion years ago, when the earth was newborn, it was a harsh, unadorned world of water, gravel, and rock. Geological dates, particularly at the dawn of time, must be understood as approximate and tentative. At any moment new evidence may be found and the evolutionary calendar will once again be revised—much to the embarrassment of science writers. Such dates, however, sketch the broad perspectives of time and enable us to regard the human adventure with both the humility and awe it deserves. It is believed that for at least half of geologic time the earth was uninhabited by even the simplest form of life. The great variety of living creatures which have since swarmed across its face and settled in its cracks and crevices has probably evolved in approximately two billion years. Not until the last few minutes of geological time, perhaps a million years ago, did man arrive, and he has been civilized for no more than six thousand years.

From the evidence of a restless, changing universe and from the pattern of our evolving planet, it is hardly right to conclude that evolution is a process designed to culminate in *Homo sapiens*; that man, having climbed to the top of the evolutionary ladder, is a final and perfect product. On the other hand, since the arrival of man nothing on earth has been quite the same. Never before has a single species gained supreme power over all the other species of this planet. No other species, no giant insect, no walking, tool-making dolphin, no superape, nor any creature that may yet evolve is likely to topple man from his throne. Man is so powerful that he would never tolerate the development of a species superior to himself but would direct his own evolution to incorporate the characteristics he desires.

The reason man is able to influence his own evolution is because of evolution's most glorious achievement—the human brain. Since our brain is the biological organ of curiosity and prediction, it is quite fitting at this point to ask certain questions about the future: Now that man has begun to explore the contents of his skull, in what direction are his investigations likely to lead? What is the future of the brain as an organ of the body? Will it continue to evolve? Finally, what is the future of the species which, having acquired a human brain, roams this earth in uneasy triumph and dares to replace the blind force of nature with something better—or worse?

In the Laboratory

In recent years man has made dramatic progress in unraveling the mysteries of his brain, yet this incredibly intricate jungle of nerve cells still remains a dark continent. We can expect that research on the electrical and chemical properties of the brain, studies of its individual nerve cells, and investigations of the brain's submicroscopic molecular structure will make major contributions to our knowledge of the brain's behavior in sickness and in health. Neurologists hope to learn how to regenerate diseased or injured nerve fibers in the central nervous system; the role of genetic defects as a cause of mental retardation has only begun to be explored; and there is an urgent need to learn the secrets of the complex neurological disorders which bring heartache and suffering to approximately one out of eight individuals in the United States alone.

The dream of solving the riddle of memory and learning has at last become a laboratory project. Electronic tools are busily probing the machinery of in-

stinct and emotion, and scientists speak enthusiastic-
ally of using precise electrical and chemical techniques
to control the cerebral sources of human behavior. It
is also possible that as we learn more about the relationship between the brain—including its sensory
organs—and our mental experiences, we shall narrow
the gap which separates physiological and psychological events. On one side of this artificial barrier stands
the biological animal, on the other the psychological
animal, and the mystery which has baffled man since
ancient times is how these twin creatures speak to each
other.

Before a definitive account of the brain and its relationship to human behavior can be given, many more
pieces of the puzzle must still be found. It is entirely
possible that the task may involve more than the difficult matter of filling in the missing parts of an outline.
The outline itself may have to be altered, for there are
certain problems which have thus far resisted all attempts at explanation by existing scientific concepts.
The problem of relating electrical impulses to the experience of seeing a tree or generating a good intention
is one of these. In addition, there are the unexplained
and scientifically embarrassing phenomena of parapsychology. Known by such names as *extrasensory perception* (ESP), including telepathy, clairvoyance, and
precognition, and *psychokinesis* (PK), these "psi"
experiences, as they are called, suggest that a special

kind of communication may exist between human beings and their environment (other people, events, and inanimate objects). This communication "system" appears neither to use the ordinary sensorimotor pathways in our nervous system nor to follow the rules of time and space as we know them today.

Although there are many charlatans in this highly constroversial field, much serious work is being done by honest, objective investigators who in fact make it their business to expose cases of fraud and hoax. Merely because we cannot explain such phenomena and because the data stubbornly refuse to accommodate themselves to the framework of our knowledge, we do not have the right to discard such inconvenient information. The voice of skepticism raised by tradition and convention is always loud. Although the "psi" phenomena are no more than a whisper, they hint that all may not be well with our concepts as they exist today. It would certainly not be the first time in the history of science that stubborn problems and persistent contradictions have finally forced the revision or expansion of established beliefs. At the turn of this century Albert Einstein, unable to reconcile certain troublesome scientific inconsistencies, jolted the tidy world of Newtonian physics by unlocking a theoretical door through which scientists then poured in pursuit of the knowledge which lay on the other side. Similarly, it is not impossible that the brain still awaits its "Einstein" and that eventually our knowledge of the brain will include chapters whose titles we cannot even imagine today.

The Evolving Brain

In brain and in bodily structure we are not basically different from the earliest members of our species. For lack of sufficient fossil evidence, the exact age of Homo sapiens is debatable. He may be 200,000 years old; there is no question that 25,000 years ago, the tall, handsome Cro-Magnon hunters and artists were in brain and body entirely modern. This, however, is no reason to believe that the brain has stopped evolving, for as a species Homo sapiens is a newcomer, and as evolutionary time goes, modern man has presided over this planet for a relatively short time.

Anthropologists believe that aside from certain minor changes such as the continued loss of bodily hair, alterations in his facial bones, and a somewhat better adjustment to his erect posture, man's basic body structure will change very little in the near future, for his brain has made further structural specialization unnecessary. Throughout its history the human hand has remained the same, for man's tools have eliminated the need for growing biological tweezers, spades, and soup spoons. This does not mean that man has escaped from the forces of natural selection by which he changes biologically in response to his environment. Rather it is the environment which man has succeeded in altering, adapting it to his needs and to his limitations. In the rapidly changing world of modern society it is by no means a simple matter to determine which of the traits we inherit will in the long run be desirable. Defects in eyesight and deficiencies in vision are not a serious concern to man, for these are easily corrected by eyeglasses, telescopes, and microscopes. Although brute force and a strong arm have often secured victory in the "struggle" for survival, in many primitive cultures and certainly in modern society, the "fit" who are to survive may be those who can control their fists and who are endowed with the biological ingredients of foresight, restraint, and cooperation.

Since it is generally agreed that man will depend increasingly on his brain for survival and that he will use his intellect to direct the course of his cultural (nongenetic) evolution, it is expected that man's major biological (genetic) evolution will take place in his brain and nervous system. The ancient method of natural selection will continue to operate, but today man is also preparing to intervene directly in the management of his own genetic affairs.

He has already learned how to influence the heredity of his domestic plants and animals through the control of their breeding patterns, but this method is relatively slow and crude and, as a technique for human beings, morally distasteful. It is predicted that in time man will be able to "touch" the genetic material itself, manipulating his own heredity with considerably more speed and precision than would be possible in the method of selective breeding. By rearranging or altering the actual structure of his own chromosomes and genes, man should be able to alter specific traits and characteristics with predictable results. The significance of such an achievement would be profound. Eventually man may be able to improve the inefficient, often haphazard process by which nature produces gifted individuals and creative geniuses. Even more, scientists hope to correct genetic errors within the blueprints of the cell itself and thus directly intercept the defective hereditary chain which results in so much human tragedy and waste.

Inevitably the brain will continue to evolve, but it is believed that the changes produced by natural selection will not be dramatic. They are more likely to be minor adaptations in the direction already charted. To this reasonable prediction there is a possible exception. The by-products and side effects of the great technological power man wields are not necessarily advantageous to him. By enabling individuals with physical defects to survive and reproduce, we have interfered with nature's system of genetic housecleaning—a ruthless but apparently successful technique. Despite the risk, we would not have it otherwise, for an important condition of man's human status is that ideally he values his moral well-being above his physical health. However, in his newly acquired power to tinker with the atom, man has become involved, whether he likes

it or not, in a complex and dangerous game. Radiation
is known to affect the genetic structure of the cell. If
man, unrestrained, continues to pollute the air he
breathes and to contaminate the food he eats with
hazardous quantities of radioactive materials, no one
knows what effect the increased exposure to radiation
will eventually have on his descendants.

Barring such genetic disaster and temporarily ignoring the dismal fact that man, like a child playing with
matches, may suddenly remove himself from this
planet—along with a goodly part of evolution's supposedly lesser works—we can predict the future of
man's brain from the trends it has followed in the past.

Although it is not impossible that entirely new cerebral structures might appear, there is no need to develop a brain highly specialized for the performance of
certain routine tasks. For just as man has provided his
body with tools, so too will he build tools for his brain.
The work of memory and calculating wizards can be
handled by computers, and the physician of the future
will be appreciated not so much for his ability to store
and recall the routine details of diagnosis and therapy
as for those qualities of judgment, insight, and understanding which are the unique possession of the living
human brain.

It is unlikely that a new human species with a super-
sized brain will suddenly arise, for there are certain
practical limitations which cannot be ignored. A very
much larger brain, with many more cells to be wired,

would need additional time for its primary education and would require radical alterations in human anatomy and physiology—changes which at this point no longer seem likely. To permit the birth of a giant brain it would be necessary to enlarge the pelvic opening, and the human life span itself would have to be prolonged, lest the brain emerge from an extended childhood only to perform the last act of a tragicomedy—its long apprenticeship all in vain, time, alas, having run out.

The genetic evolution of the brain is expected to follow the course known as *foetalization*, by which the adult individual retains those youthful physical qualities which at one time, as in the case of the disappointing ape, appeared only in the young of a species. From ape to man-ape and from the brutish Pithecanthropines to Homo sapiens, the jaws and teeth have continued to retreat, the skull bones have become thinner and the forehead less sloping. Compared to the size of its skull, the face of the human infant is relatively small and its features sketchy and incomplete. As his face and jaws continue to shrink in size, the man of the future will appear even more childlike, delicate, and, ironically, innocent in appearance. A smaller face would permit still more head structure to be devoted to housing a larger brain, and above the smaller face of our descendants there may loom a relatively majestic—although hairless—cranial vault (see Fig. 25).

While generations to come may face the future with

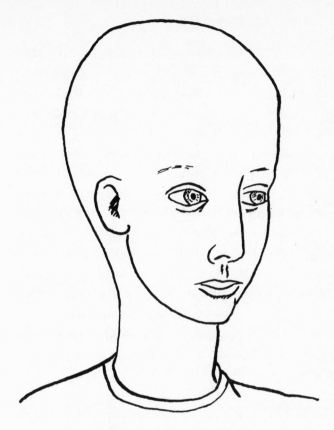

Fig. 25 *Man of the future*

less face and more brain and the radiance of love will
be forced to shine in diminished quarters, the value of
an additional quota of brain cells or the possession of
a brain with a cranial capacity of 2000 instead of 1400
cc. is not so simple to estimate. There have already
been human brains larger than our own, and despite a nerve cell count which makes our brain look
impoverished, the whale, for other reasons, has re-

mained behind in the evolutionary scramble. We know that it is not merely the size of the human brain or the number of its cells which is significant, but rather the way man uses—or neglects—his initial endowment of some ten billion cortical nerve cells.

To wish for a bigger brain containing more cells is to miss the point. We already possess a "better" brain and have a sufficient number of brain cells, but ironically these gifts may be wasted on human beings, who too often fail to understand what a brain is for and neglect and squander its gifts. Modern man cannot afford the luxury of waiting for improved cerebral equipment to sprout inside his skull, for he is running out of time. The future of the human brain—indeed of man himself—depends on what man does with his brain today, lest there be no future, or none that man would care to contemplate.

Man Takes Over

Despite considerable skill in performing intricate tasks, insects and computers—to use two extreme examples—are limited in what they can do. No electronic computer, while solving the equations which mark the route to the moon, was ever inspired to compose a sonnet to that lovely celestial body; no bee ever decided to make plastic instead of wax or jam instead of honey. Only partially inscribed at birth and completed later while "on the job," man's adaptable and versatile brain is the biological instrument which permits choice. Because the patterns of human behavior are not inevitable, because choice and possibility are inherent in the design of the human brain, so too is freedom one of its fundamental provisions—freedom to turn one way or another, to create blossom or blight, to hate and yet repent, and to enrich or impoverish his planet. Endowed by his brain with vast power over his environment, man controls floods and makes the desert bloom, he creates artificial environments in space suits and incubators, and when his side of the planet turns its back upon the sun, he defies the primordial night by lighting his candle or electric bulb. Truly, freedom is power—but it is the power to do wrong as well as right.

Biological freedom would be a useless, in fact dangerous gift were the brain unable to learn, to profit from experience, and to communicate knowledge to others. The genetic system of inheritance makes it possible to pass instructions concerning characteristics such as the color of the eyes or the shape of the nose from one generation to the next. But the well-developed muscles of the athlete or the knowledge of table manners and nuclear physics acquired after birth cannot travel the genetic route from parent to child. His brain, however, enables man to communicate acquired information and attitudes from one generation to another as well as to the members of the same generation. The mother teaches her child how to use his fork or chopsticks, the athlete transmits, if not his well-trained muscles, at least his enthusiasm and special athletic skills, and from our teachers and from books we inherit a considerable part of the accumulated experience of past centuries. This form of inheritance is called learning, and the information which is communicated from brain to brain, instead of gene to gene, is known as culture.

As the guiding force in evolution, nature is not always wise. Judged by human standards, the system of natural selection is frequently guilty of error, waste, and inefficiency. The extravagantly built dinosaurs turned out to be an unsuccessful experiment, and the marvelous human body is nevertheless a complex playground for mischief, illustrating poor planning, contradiction, and outmoded design. Although nature blunders down blind alleys, although she makes genetic errors, often leaving disaster in her wake, although her trial and error methods would appall human efficiency experts, not for a moment should we underestimate the magnificence of nature's accomplishment. To breathe life into a clump of restless molecules drifting in the primeval "soup" and to turn them after some two billion years into the complicated, intelligent, and ambitious organism known as a human being is, from beginning to end, more than we know how to do.

As a "director" of evolution, man, in contrast to nature, is precocious and impatient. He has the advantage of knowing what he wants and he has some idea of how to get it. His efforts are therefore consciously directed and supposedly intelligent. If he requires animals and plants suited to life in dry, arid regions, he need not wait hundreds of years for successful species to evolve. Instead he gives nature a helping hand by artificially selecting for breeding those specimens with desirable characteristics, eliminating those which do not serve his purposes. Like nature, man is not necessarily wise, but unlike nature, he works with phenomenal speed. His handiwork swiftly affects vast numbers of individuals, and for better or worse, it registers in the composition of his planet and in the atmosphere surrounding it. Gifted and conscious of his goals, but powerful and impetuous, man can less and less afford to make mistakes.

And Finds Himself in Trouble

The difference between nature's time scale for designing and decorating this earth and man's schedule for his lesser works is startling. For a long time, probably more than two billion years, there was no life at all on this planet. First the earth had to become a more hospitable place, and then in her turbulent, watery laboratory nature needed time to perform the original experiments by which the first organic molecules were created. From the dawn of life in the obscure beginnings of Pre-Cambrian time to the period of its earliest fossil records, almost a billion and a half years elapsed in which the changes, although of extreme importance, do not seem to have been particularly dramatic. About

500 million years ago, at the edge of the Cambrian period, the pace quickened so that in a mere half billion years the route from sponges, ancient worms, and crablike trilobites to man was traversed. Then in a geological blink of an eye, man advanced from making primitive hand axes to bouncing light beams off the moon. What is more, most of man's remarkable achievements were created in a fraction of the last second. The development of the airplane is a striking illustration of the speed of modern scientific and technological progress. In less than fifty years the primitive airplane has evolved to forms of aircraft which travel faster than the speed of sound and space ships which hurtle through celestial regions still forbidden to birds some 150 million years after their debut on earth.

At this whirlwind pace it is essential that man acquire the wisdom he lacks, and he must do so quickly, for it is his own destiny which is at stake. In this century man has gained unprecedented power and his toys and gadgets have a global bounce and screech. Where once he cleared a dozen trees to pitch his camp, he now erects a great city on forest graveyards of his own creation. Where formerly he built a little fire which sent its thin column of smoke curling upward, today he constructs a mighty industrial plant which belches its black sewage into the air he breathes. And while he scurries about his planet, crowding it and scarring and maiming it, he harvests the bounty within its crust and waters with little thought that such supplies may not be endless.

The equation between human ingenuity and human wisdom has become dangerously unbalanced. If long ago man invented a spear and then used it unwisely, the most damage he could do was to kill, one at a time, a number of his fellow men. If he waged war, the enemy was relatively close at hand, while elsewhere in other corners of the wilderness, downstream or across the earth, other human beings carried on the more civilized affairs of mankind until it was their turn to play the spear game. Modern weapons reflect the evil face of man's technological genius, for with one strike they can kill thousands of individuals. Even a brief thermonuclear tournament might destroy or devastate all life on this planet, including innocent plant and animal bystanders. With the gift of power goes the burden of responsibility. The more power man wields the more he has need of understanding, self-control, and the unselfishness to behave in such a way today that the human species may survive and future generations may have reason to speak of us with kindness and respect.

The Unbalanced Equation

In reviewing man's achievement it is tempting to conclude that he has been making progress, to believe that he has improved, and so to trust that inevitably he will become more intelligent, wiser, and more humane. Many people question this concept of biological progress. They point out that it is the things which man has created or invented—his airplanes, weapons, drugs—which have "progressed" or improved and that what we mistake for progress is only the accumulation of experience and knowledge, of tools and gadgets. That the harnessing of atomic energy required more intelligence than the taming of fire in an ancient world of superstition, ignorance, and terror is unlikely. Whether the invention of the light bulb demanded greater genius than the invention of the wheel is highly doubtful; and although we have the advantage of centuries of collected knowledge, what person living today would claim to be more intelligent than Aristotle or wiser than Socrates?

The washing machine has made remarkable progress, but we are in danger of deceiving ourselves if we assume that wisdom and understanding have similarly improved or that human nature has grown more humane. It has been observed that what we often mistake for improvement may simply be the lack of temptation. Certainly the atrocities of World War II, the evil practices of modern tyrants, and man's continued inhumanity to his fellow man easily rival the worst brutality of so-called savages. Too often when the chips are down, man's civilized garments dissolve and the brute beneath is revealed. If now and then a primitive cannibal dined on a tasty enemy, he was at least limited by his appetite. That modern victims die in gas chambers and slave labor camps instead is no evidence of improved morality. It may indicate only that cannibalism is impractical for the wholesale extermination of human beings.

According to this concept we are just as wise or foolish, intelligent or stupid, noble or brutal as man was in his primitive condition. It is difficult to say whether the "equation" between human wisdom and understanding and human inventiveness and technical genius has ever been balanced, but in the past the harm man could do was limited. Today a sudden increase in man's power threatens to upset the working equilibrium between his ingenuity and his ability to control himself—a relationship which although far from perfect, has until now stumbled along with a reasonable degree of success. Power so vast that it can swiftly devastate an entire planet obviously can no longer be managed by old-fashioned quantities of wisdom and restraint or by a morality which operates sometimes, and sometimes not. In a high-speed era where a second chance may not be offered and where we cannot afford fools in high places, it is risky to hope that the growth of wisdom, understanding, and cooperation are an inevitable genetic consequence and that it is nature's intention to rescue us from our predicament.

It is up to man to help himself. Using his wits to solve his problems is an ancient human tradition, but man's efforts, often admirable in intent, have in practice been fumbling and expensive. Now that he has begun to study his brain, it seems reasonable to expect that he pay attention to its appetites, its limitations, and its special talents. We heed the demands of our hearts and muscles, we are taught to respect the body's nutritional requirements, and the females of our species lavish loving care on their purely decorative hair. Yet even today concern for the brain as a hard-working organ of the body is left to man's better but unpredictable instincts and to a superficial knowledge of human behavior. Ignorance is rarely an advantage. Trusting less to chance and depending more on a growing understanding of the brain as a biological organ, man may eventually learn to use his brain more intelligently and therefore more profitably.

Almost anyone can be taught to drive a car, but in the long run we use the vehicle more effectively if we understand its purpose, how it operates, and the conditions which are harmful to it. A car can neither fly nor swim, and human legs are frequently better suited to navigating crowded city streets. Gasoline is the machine's fuel, oil and water are essential to its well-being, abuse shortens the life of its brakes and gears, and when the automobile is neglected its parts corrode and rust. The neglected or abused brain suffers comparable ills. We do not know the physiology of imagination and creativity, nor have we discovered the neural secrets of wisdom, generosity, and compassion. But it is time we turned in our magic wands, abandoned superstition and wishful thinking, and examined the perplexities of human behavior in terms of the biological organ which plays the greatest role in directing it.

The Private Mirror

The brain and the entire nervous system determine the way in which we perceive and interpret the world in which we live. For sound physiological and psychological reasons, the same image is by no means shared by everyone—a truth of which world leaders often seem tragically ignorant. It is a serious mistake to assume that individual perception provides a true report of the environment since what we choose not to see or what we fail to observe is forever missing from what we mistakenly call reality. Experiments have demonstrated that in sensory inputs ranging from simple sensations of sound and light to the details of historical events, emotion, expectation, and training influence the way we interpret the outside world. The blindfolded fraternity initiate, told he is about to swallow a juicy worm, gags on harmless spaghetti, which he would ordinarily identify with ease from its taste, form, and texture. Treachery at the home office in the brain is not the only cause of sensory deception. It has been shown that emotions and experience can also modify the sensory signals within the sense organs themselves and along the incoming sensory fibers. Thus perception may be distorted at its source.

Since culture is the product of human brains, it

is essential that we respect a biological heritage which provides that individuals as well as societies shall differ in their view of the world. Tolerance and mutual understanding are more likely to thrive if we recognize that the difference in the views and values of others is not always a matter of perversity or of a lack of true enlightenment, but may derive from the fundamental provisions of man's physiological and psychological nature.

Handle With Care

As the organ of logic and reason, the brain resembles the computer in that its output can be no better than the information and instructions originally placed in its input. To set a brain to the task of solving the wrong problems and for the wrong purpose, to admire its logic while ignoring the fact that its reasoning is based on faulty premises, or to program it with false or inaccurate information is to foredoom this marvelous instrument to produce anything from minor silliness to untold human horror. Furthermore, since the structure of language influences the basic assumptions individuals and societies make about their environment, conclusions which appear logical and intelligent to one society may be totally incomprehensible to another.

The care and nurture of the living brain may in some way resemble that of the computer, but the use to which we put that brain must be entirely different. The flexibility and adaptability of the human nervous system and the freedom human behavior derives from these gifts are the qualities we cherish most. Although the ape is fated to run out of mental steam while still in his physical prime, man's youthful curiosity and imagination and his ability to question and make his own discoveries need not desert him upon reaching maturity. Insects and computers cannot dispute the instructions they inherit. But man has a brain and is expected to use it before blindly inheriting second-hand thoughts. To permit his versatile brain to operate at the level of a machine or to permit it to revert to the condition of a lower animal's in which inborn reflex and instinct rule is to insult his own brain.

The superior ability of the human brain to learn and to go its own way has always placed a heavy burden on the matter and manner of its education. In a society which finds itself increasingly knowledgeable in scientific and material affairs but uncomfortably deficient in the less tangible virtues of understanding, tolerance, and brotherly love, the need for adjusting the gap in our values grows urgent. Wherever possible we must examine education in relation to the brain which receives it and consider human behavior in terms of the organ which helps produce it.

From a study of his patients—not nerve cells—Freud recognized the importance of early childhood experiences, even those which are forgotten, in shaping an individual's personality. Now physiologists have begun to probe the brain itself in search of the biologi-

cal foundations of human behavior. Although we do
not yet know how memories are recorded, part of the
answer lies in the chemistry and physiology of the
nerve cell. In an attempt to explain the persistent and
potent quality of certain childhood experiences, one
interesting theory suggests that since the cortex, the
organ of reason and inhibition, is not fully developed
in the very young child, prejudices, irrational fears,
and the lessons of love and rejection fed to the de-
fenseless brain at this time cannot be examined critically, perhaps to be rejected or modified. Instead they
are accepted indiscriminately by the recording system
and without further editing are indelibly impressed
upon the nerve cells of the child's brain. This is only
a theory, but plainly, if the brain of the young child
is not to be seriously crippled for the performance of
its adult tasks, the physiological mechanisms of its
nerve cells must be respected.

That there is a need for a change in our values is
not a new idea. That a contradiction between what
we practice and what we preach contains the seeds
of inevitable defeat is also well known. But it is time
that education, in the nursery and in the school, at
the dinner table and at the conference table, paid closer
attention to the brain it is educating. We honor successful inventors, victorious generals, and dedicated
scientists whose discoveries are useful. And when it
works, honesty is the best policy. We do not expect
the year-old child to stand up and walk merely because

we wish it. First he must learn how; the necessary sensorimotor paths must be established in his nervous system and his brain must record the lesson. Similarly, somewhere in the child's impressionable brain cells the lessons of material success are carefully registered. To expect a brain trained from the beginning to seek material success automatically to turn later in life to the pursuit of more idealistic forms of success is to ignore the physiological facts of life. Should the owner of such a brain wish to alter his course as an adult, motivation, perseverance, and the strength of his ideals must be equal to the task of doing considerable cerebral rewiring.

In the same way, the discrepancy between our words and our deeds does not go unnoticed by the brain, however much we might wish it. What is the point of preaching the value of honesty to a child if at the same time we cheat the grocer or lie in filling out an income tax form? Along the sensory nerves to the child's brain go the lessons of dishonesty as well as honesty, and we deceive ourselves if we think that nerve cells have an inborn preference for pretty phrases and fail to register deeds. Simplifying considerably, one might imagine that first the contradictory advice reaches the child's brain and is recorded there. Eventually the child resolves this conflict according to the beast or the human being in his nature. In the course of evolution, however, the beast came first, and reason and moral virtue are recent innovations. Often it is with difficulty that the human being dominates the brute within himself. When the child discovers that society makes it difficult for him to live according to the principles it fails to uphold, he too often makes the necessary adjustments in his nervous system and cheerfully goes his way. The physiological mechanisms of compromise are undoubtedly ample: The conscious memory of the act may be erased, the interpretative offices in the cerebral cortex may edit the event so that the dishonesty is no longer perceived, or rationalizations may be constructed and new nerve routes authorized to dull the prick of conscience in the cortical cells.

A Personal Matter

Man holds his destiny in his own hands. He is his own fairy godparent, and he possesses the means with which to reduce all the mighty structure of civilization to something even less attractive than Cinderella's rags and mice. For mankind the future has already begun. With amazing speed and characteristic daring and ambition, man is hard at work sketching its outlines, but there is reason to question whether at the same time he is making certain he will be able to live in it.

The lessons of evolution teach that even the mightiest species, if it cannot adjust to the demands of its environment, is doomed to extinction. In the past, man has proven himself to be singularly gifted in solving the problems presented by his environment. But he must not forget that his environment includes himself and that today the greatest threat to man is man. Above all, it is with himself that he must learn to live.

Man's responsibilities are complex and his problems are vast, but his prospects should be bright, for at last he is beginning to understand the instrument by which he is expected to save himself—his brain. The better man understands the kind of creature he is and the more he learns about his brain, the greater chance he has to use that organ intelligently. It is within man's power not only to insure his future on this planet but to create a future graced by his own brilliant and unique virtues—a gentler, kinder, more tolerant future, and one far better suited to his needs than anything the harsh, insensible rule of nature might provide. Whereas nature operates with blind force, man proceeds with knowledge, intelligence, and a measure of conscious control over his fate. As his own navigator man suffers too often from distorted vision, but he is not blind. Whether he will earn the prematurely bestowed title *sapiens*, whether man will grow up to become wise, remains to be seen.

In the meantime, the stars hurtle outward through space, our little planet twirls upon its tilted axis, and bird and beast attend their timeless needs unconcerned, while man hurries about his risky affairs with genius in one hand and in the other, destruction.

Endowed by his brain with the biological gifts of possibility and choice, man therefore inherits both the heavy burden of responsibility and freedom's sweeter offspring, hope. If things do not turn out as he wishes, he will have no one to blame but himself. Man is his own hope.

APPENDIX

I *Classification of Chordates*
(according to Colbert)

PHYLUM: CHORDATA

Subphylum: Hemichordata (*Balanoglossus*)
Subphylum: Cephalochordata (*Amphioxus*)
Subphylum: Urochordata (sea squirts)
Subphylum: Vertebrata (the vertebrates)

Classes of the Subphylum Vertebrata
Agnatha: jawless fishes (includes lamprey and hagfishes)
Placodermi: primitive jawed fishes (all now extinct)
Chondrichthyes: cartilaginous fishes (includes sharks and rays)
Osteichthyes: bony fishes (includes true fishes and air-breathing fishes, such as lung fishes)
Amphibia: includes frogs, toads, salamanders
Reptilia: includes dinosaurs, turtles, lizards, snakes
Aves: birds
Mammalia: includes moles, bats, mice, whales, dogs, horses, camels, and the order of Primates

II *Classification of Orders of Living Placental Mammals (Eutheria)*
(according to Colbert)

There are 28 orders of Eutheria. The 16 not extinct are given here with a few representative animals:

> Insectivora: moles, hedgehogs, shrews
> Chiroptera: bats
> Dermoptera: "flying lemurs"
> Edentata: anteaters, sloths, armadillos
> Pholidota: scaly anteaters
> Primates: tree shrews (?), lemurs, tarsiers,
>   monkeys, apes, men
> Rodentia: squirrels, beavers, mice
> Lagomorpha: rabbits, hares
> Cetacea: whales, porpoises
> Carnivora: beasts of prey, such as dogs,
>   cats, foxes, seals, weasels, rac-
>   coons
> Tubulidentata: aardvarks
> Hyracoidea: rabbitlike conies of Africa and
>   the Middle East
> Proboscidea: elephants
> Sirenia: sea cows
> Perissodactyla: odd-toed hoofed mammals,
>   such as horses, zebras
> Artiodactyla: even-toed hoofed mammals,
>   such as pigs, camels, deer,
>   giraffes

III *Classification of Primates and Man*
(according to Colbert)

Order: PRIMATES: tree shrews (?), lemurs, tarsiers, monkeys,
    apes, men
Suborder: Lemuroidea: lemurs and their relatives
Suborder: Tarsioidea: tarsiers
Suborder: ANTHROPOIDEA: monkeys, apes, men

Superfamily: Ceboidea—New World monkeys
(tropical America)
Superfamily: Cercopithecoidea — Old World
monkeys (tropical Asia, Africa)
Superfamily: HOMINOIDEA—apes and men
Family: Parapithecidae—*Parapithecus*
Family: Pongidae—gibbons, dryopithecines,
chimpanzees, orangutans, gorillas
Family: HOMINIDAE—men

SUGGESTIONS
FOR FURTHER READING

Adler, Irving, THINKING MACHINES: A LAYMAN'S INTRODUCTION TO LOGIC, BOOLEAN ALGEBRA AND COMPUTERS. New York, John Day Company, 1961. (Signet Science Library, 1962).

Auerbach, Charlotte, THE SCIENCE OF GENETICS. New York, Harper & Brothers, 1961.
An excellent survey of modern genetics including laws of heredity and recent studies of the gene. Useful drawings and diagrams.

Berrill, N. J., MAN'S EMERGING MIND. New York, Dodd, Mead & Company, 1955.
Deals with the evolution of the human brain and mind. A charming and thoughtful treatment.

Best, Charles H., and Taylor, Norman B., THE LIVING BODY: A TEXT IN HUMAN PHYSIOLOGY, 4th ed. New York, Holt, Rinehart & Winston, 1958.
An excellent basic text written by the authors of the standard work on physiology used in medical schools.

Cannon, Walter B., THE WISDOM OF THE BODY, 2nd ed. New York, W. W. Norton & Company, 1939.
A classic. See for discussion of homeostasis and the role of the autonomic nervous system.

Carlson, Anton J., and Johnson, Victor, THE MACHINERY OF THE BODY, 5th ed. Chicago, University of Chicago Press, 1961.

A lucid, well-organized introductory textbook of physiology. Useful illustrations.

Eccles, John C., "The Physiology of Imagination." *Scientific American*, (September, 1958), pp. 135–146.
Semi-technical but fascinating description of the hypothetical neural routes underlying the creative processes.

Eisley, Loren, THE IMMENSE JOURNEY. New York, Random House (Vintage Books), 1957.
Beautifully written, highly personal essays on the relationship between man and nature both now and in the past.

Hawkes, Jacquetta, MAN ON EARTH. New York, Random House, 1955.
A lively, poetic account of human evolution, the development of the brain, and the rise of civilization and culture.

Hockett, Charles F., "The Origin of Speech." *Scientific American*, (September, 1960), pp. 89–96.
The evolution of human language and its relationship to the communication systems used by animals.

Lilly, John C., MAN AND DOLPHIN. New York, Doubleday & Co., 1961.
Extremely interesting. Dr. Lilly is an authority on dolphins and their methods of communication.

Pfeiffer, John, THE HUMAN BRAIN. New York, Harper & Brothers, 1955.
Readable and reliable. Includes several interesting chapters on recent research in mental illness.

Sherrington, Sir Charles, MAN ON HIS NATURE, 2nd ed. New York, Doubleday & Company (Anchor Books), 1955.
A difficult book but a classic of modern scientific literature. See Chapter 7, particularly pages 183–184, for the

source of the often quoted description of the brain as a "great ravelled knot" and an "enchanted loom."

Simpson, George Gaylord, THE MEANING OF EVOLUTION. New Haven, Yale University Press, 1949. (Yale Paperbound, 1960)
A clear and authoritative account of the nature and meaning of evolution and of the history of life on this planet.

Walter, W. Grey, THE LIVING BRAIN. New York, W. W. Norton & Company, 1953.
A witty and fascinating discussion of the electrical properties of the brain and their significance. Includes detailed descriptions of electronic "animals" built by the author.

Wendt, Herbert, THE ROAD TO MAN. New York, Doubleday & Company, 1959.
Evolution from the dawn of life to the rise of thought. Interesting photographs.

BIBLIOGRAPHY

Books

Adler, Irving, THINKING MACHINES. New York, New American Library (Signet Science Library), 1962.

Adrian, E. D., Bremer, F., and Jasper, H., eds., BRAIN MECHANISMS AND CONSCIOUSNESS: A SYMPOSIUM. Oxford, Blackwell Scientific Publications, 1954.

Ashley-Montagu, M. F., THE DIRECTION OF HUMAN DEVELOPMENT. New York, Harper & Brothers, 1955.

——— MAN: HIS FIRST MILLION YEARS. Cleveland, World Publishing Company, 1957.

Berrill, N. J., MAN'S EMERGING MIND. New York, Dodd, Mead & Company, 1955.

Best, Charles H., and Taylor, Norman B., THE PHYSIOLOGICAL BASIS OF MEDICAL PRACTICE, 7th ed. Baltimore, Williams & Wilkins Company, 1961, pp. 1137–1312.

Black, Max, ed., THE IMPORTANCE OF LANGUAGE. New Jersey, Prentice-Hall (Spectrum Book), 1962.

Bonin, Gerhardt von, ESSAY ON THE CEREBRAL CORTEX. Springfield, Ill., Charles Thomas, 1950.

Borek, Ernest, MAN THE CHEMICAL MACHINE. New York, Columbia University Press, 1952.

Buchsbaum, Ralph, ANIMALS WITHOUT BACKBONES: AN INTRODUCTION TO THE INVERTEBRATES, rev. ed. Chicago, University of Chicago Press, 1948.

Buddenbrock, Wolfgang von, THE SENSES. Ann Arbor, University of Michigan Press, 1958.

Cannon, Walter B., THE WISDOM OF THE BODY, 2nd ed. New York, W. W. Norton & Company, 1939.

Carlson, Anton J., and Johnson, Victor, THE MACHINERY OF THE BODY, 2nd ed. Chicago, University of Chicago Press, 1941.

Colbert, Edwin H., EVOLUTION OF THE VERTEBRATES. New York, Science Editions, Inc., 1961.

Dobzhansky, Theodosius, EVOLUTION, GENETICS, AND MAN. New York, John Wiley & Sons, 1955.

Eccles, John C., THE NEUROPHYSIOLOGICAL BASIS OF MIND. Oxford, Clarendon Press, 1953.

Eisley, Loren, THE IMMENSE JOURNEY. New York, Random House (Vintage Books), 1957.

Fletcher, Ronald, INSTINCT IN MAN. New York, International Universities Press, Inc., 1957.

Gamow, George, ONE TWO THREE . . . INFINITY. New York, New American Library (Mentor Book), 1954.

Grinker, Roy, Bucy, Paul, and Sahs, Adolph, NEUROLOGY, 5th ed. Springfield, Ill., Charles Thomas, 1960.

Harrison, T., et al, eds. PRINCIPLES OF INTERNAL MEDICINE, 3rd ed. Vol. 1. New York, McGraw-Hill Book Company, 1958, pp. 228–408.

Herrick, Judson C., THE EVOLUTION OF HUMAN NATURE. Austin, University of Texas Press, 1956.

Huxley, Thomas H., MAN'S PLACE IN NATURE. Ann Arbor, University of Michigan Press (Ann Arbor Paperback), 1959.

International Business Machines Corp., GENERAL INFORMATION MANUAL. New York, 1960.
——— NEW METHODS FOR KNOWING. New York, 1960.

Jones, Frederick W., and Porteus, Stanley, THE MATRIX OF THE MIND. Honolulu, University of Hawaii Press, 1928.

Kitay, J., and Altschule, M., THE PINEAL GLAND. Cambridge, Harvard University Press, 1954.

Koenigswald, G. H. R. von, MEETING PREHISTORIC MAN. New York, Harper & Brothers, 1957.

La Barre, Weston, THE HUMAN ANIMAL. Chicago, University of Chicago Press, 1954.

Lapp, Ralph, MAN AND SPACE. New York, Harper & Brothers, 1961.

Laslett, Peter, ed., THE PHYSICAL BASIS OF MIND. Oxford, Basil Blackwell, 1950.

Lassek, A. M., THE HUMAN BRAIN: FROM PRIMITIVE TO MODERN. Springfield, Ill., Charles Thomas, 1957.

Lilly, John C., MAN AND DOLPHIN. New York, Doubleday & Company, 1961.

Linton, Ralph, THE TREE OF CULTURE. New York, Alfred A. Knopf, Inc., 1955.

Medawar, P. B., THE FUTURE OF MAN. New York, New American Library (Mentor Book), 1961.

Mellersh, H. E. L., THE STORY OF LIFE. New York, G. P. Putnam's Sons, 1958.

Mitchell, Philip H., A TEXTBOOK OF GENERAL PHYSIOLOGY. New York, McGraw-Hill Book Company, 1956.

Moody, Paul Ames, INTRODUCTION TO EVOLUTION, 2nd ed. New York, Harper & Row, 1962.

Morgan, Clifford, and Stellar, Eliot, PHYSIOLOGICAL PSYCHOLOGY, 2nd ed. New York, McGraw-Hill Book Company, 1950.

Netter, Frank, NERVOUS SYSTEM. New Jersey, Ciba Collection of Medical Illustrations, Ciba Pharmaceutical Products, Inc., 1953.

Neumann, John von, THE COMPUTER AND THE BRAIN. New Haven, Yale University Press, 1958.

Penfield, Wilder, and Rasmussen, T., THE CEREBRAL CORTEX OF MAN. New York, Macmillan, 1950.

Perry, Ralph B., REALMS OF VALUE: A CRITIQUE OF HUMAN CIVILIZATION. Cambridge, Harvard University Press, 1954.

Pfeiffer, John, THE HUMAN BRAIN. New York, Harper & Brothers, 1955.

Ransom, S. W., and Clark, S. L., THE ANATOMY OF THE NERVOUS SYSTEM. Philadelphia, W. B. Saunders & Company, 1959.

Rush, J. H., THE DAWN OF LIFE. New York, New American Library (Signet Science Library), 1962.

Schachtel, Ernest G., METAMORPHOSIS: ON THE DEVELOPMENT OF AFFECT, PERCEPTION, ATTENTION AND MEMORY. New York, Basic Books, Inc., 1959.

Sherrington, Sir Charles, MAN ON HIS NATURE, 2nd ed. New York, Doubleday & Company (Anchor Books), 1955.

Simpson, George Gaylord, LIFE OF THE PAST: AN INTRODUCTION TO PALEONTOLOGY. New Haven, Yale University Press, 1953.

———— THE MEANING OF EVOLUTION: A STUDY OF THE HISTORY OF LIFE AND OF ITS SIGNIFICANCE FOR MAN. New Haven, Yale University Press, 1949. (Yale Paperbound, 1960)

Sinnott, Edmund W., MATTER, MIND AND MAN: THE BIOLOGY OF HUMAN NATURE. New York, Atheneum, 1962.

Smith, Homer, FROM FISH TO PHILOSOPHER: THE STORY OF OUR INTERNAL ENVIRONMENT. New Jersey, Ciba Pharmaceutical Products, Inc., 1959.

Stagner, Ross, and Karwoski, T. F., PSYCHOLOGY. New York, McGraw-Hill Book Company, 1952.

Teilhard de Chardin, Pierre, THE PHENOMENON OF MAN. New York, Harper & Brothers, 1959.

Tokay, Elbert, THE HUMAN BODY AND HOW IT WORKS. New York, New American Library (Signet Key Book), 1961.

Walshe, F. M. R., DISEASES OF THE NERVOUS SYSTEM. Baltimore, Williams & Wilkins Company, 1947.

Walter, W. Grey, THE LIVING BRAIN. New York, W. W. Norton & Company, 1953.

Wendt, Herbert, THE ROAD TO MAN. New York, Doubleday & Company, 1959.

Wiener, Norbert, THE HUMAN USE OF HUMAN BEINGS: CYBERNETICS AND SOCIETY. New York, Doubleday & Company (Anchor Books), 1954.

Articles

Adams, Charles W., "Computer Characteristics Revisited." *Datamation*, (November, 1962).

Adams, Raymond D., "Sleep and Its Abnormalities," in T. R. Harrison, *et al*, eds, *Principles of Internal Medicine*, Vol. 1, 3rd ed. New York, McGraw-Hill Book Company, 1958, pp. 316–323.
——— "Affections of Speech." *Ibid.*, pp. 366–376.

Bunge, Mario, "Do Computers Think?" *The British Journal for the Philosophy of Science* (Edinburgh), (November, 1956).

Cobb, Stanley, "On the Nature and Locus of Mind." *Arch. Neurology and Psychiatry*, Vol. 67, No. 2, (February, 1952).

Crick, F. H. C., "The Genetic Code." *Scientific American*, (October, 1962).

Danto, Arthur C., "On Consciousness in Machines," in Sidney Hook, ed., DIMENSIONS OF MIND: A SYMPOSIUM. New York, Collier Books, 1961.

Dobzhansky, Theodosius, "The Present Evolution of Man." *Scientific American*, (September, 1960).

Eccles, John C., "The Physiology of Imagination." *Scientific American*, (September, 1958).

"Exploring the Brain of Man." National Committee for Research in Neurological Disorders, A. B. Baker, Chairman. (Brochure).

French, J. D., "Reticular Formation." *Scientific American*, (May, 1957).

Funkenstein, Daniel H., "The Physiology of Fear and Anger." *Scientific American*, (May, 1955).

Gerard, R. W., "The Brain: Mechanism of the Mind," in Lyman Bryson, ed., AN OUTLINE OF MAN'S KNOWLEDGE OF THE MODERN WORLD. New York, Nelson Doubleday, Inc., 1960.

Gibbs, Frederic Andrews, "The Most Important Thing." *American Journal of Public Health*, Vol. 41, 1951.

Gray, George W., "The Great Ravelled Knot," *Scientific American*, (October, 1949).

Harlow, Harry F., "Functional Organization of the Brain in Relation to Mentation and Behavior," in Milbank Memorial Fund, THE BIOLOGY OF MENTAL HEALTH AND DISEASE. New York, Paul B. Hoeber, Inc., Harper & Brothers, 1952.

Hockett, Charles F., "The Origin of Speech." *Scientific American*, (September, 1960).

Inge, William Ralph, "The Idea of Progress," in OUTSPOKEN ESSAYS, 2nd ser. New York, Longmans, Green & Co., 1923.

Katz, Bernhard, "Nerve Impulse," in THE PHYSICS AND CHEMISTRY OF LIFE. New York, Simon and Schuster, 1955.

Lindsley, Donald B., "Emotion," in S. S. Stevens, HANDBOOK OF EXPERIMENTAL PSYCHOLOGY. New York, John Wiley & Sons, 1951.

Livingston, Robert, "Perception and Commitment." *Bulletin of the Atomic Scientists*, (February, 1963).

Maskin, Meyer, "The Science of Personality," in Lyman Bryson, ed., AN OUTLINE OF MAN'S KNOWLEDGE OF THE MODERN WORLD. New York, Nelson Doubleday, Inc., 1960.

Ogle, Kenneth N., "The Visual Space Sense." *Science*, Vol. 135, No. 3506 (March, 1962).

Olds, James, "Pleasure Centers in the Brain." *Scientific American*, (October, 1956).

Penfield, Wilder, "Memory Mechanisms." *Arch. Neurology and Psychiatry*, Vol. 67, No. 2, 1952.

Rajchman, Jan A., "A Survey of Computer Memories." *Datamation*, (December, 1962).

Rhine, J. B., "On Parapsychology and the Nature of Man," in Sidney Hook, ed., DIMENSIONS OF MIND: A SYMPOSIUM. New York, Collier Books, 1961.

Schiller, Francis, "Consciousness Reconsidered." *Arch. Neurology and Psychiatry*, Vol. 67, No. 2, 1952.

Scriven, Michael, "The Compleat Robot: A Prologomena to Androidology," in Sidney Hook, ed., DIMENSIONS OF MIND: A SYMPOSIUM. New York, Collier Books, 1961.

Shapiro, Harry L., "What Man Will Be Like in 101,961 A.D." *The New York Times Magazine Section*, (August 13, 1961).

Sherrington, Sir Charles, "Mystery of Mysteries—The Human Brain." *Ibid.* (December 4, 1949).

Sperry, P. W., "Neurology and the Mind Brain Problem." *American Scientist*, Vol. 40, 1952.

Walshe, F. M. R., "Thoughts on the Equation of Mind with Brain." *Brain*, Vol. 76, No. 1, 1953.

Washburn, Sherwood L., "Tools and Human Evolution." *Scientific American*, (September, 1960).

Wiener, Norbert, "The Brain and the Machine," in Sidney Hook, ed., DIMENSIONS OF MIND: A SYMPOSIUM. New York, Collier Books, 1961.

Wolff, Harold G., "The Mind Body Relationship," in Lyman Bryson, ed., AN OUTLINE OF MAN'S KNOWLEDGE OF THE MODERN WORLD. New York, Nelson Doubleday, Inc., 1960.

INDEX

(Figures in boldface indicate pages upon which illustrations appear.)

Java man, 30, 36

language, value of, 13; *see also* speech
learning, 174–182, 193; as cultural inheritance, 263–264; definitions of, 178, 180–181; kinds of, 178–180; synaptic junctions in, 181–182; theoretical circuits of, 140–141; and thinking, 177–178; *see also* computer(s); conditional reflex; habit; memory
lemur, 21, 24, 25, 35
lie detector, 114, 136–137
localization of function, 10, 101, 102, 103–106
logic, *see* reasoning

Machina speculatrix, 236–238
machine, *see* computer(s)
man:
age of, 35–37, 252; civilized, 252; and evolution, 249–250, 252–253, 264–267; future appearance of, 261; future evolution of brain, 252–253, 256–262; future progress of, 267–271, 276–278; *see also* Homo sapiens
man-apes, 4, 33, 34
medulla, adrenal, 117
medulla oblongata, 85, 86, 87, 115, 116, 123
memory:
in animals, 38–39, 174–175; components of, compared to computer, 246; and consciousness, 163; in the elderly, 183; and emotion, 184; and forgetting, 187–188; and frontal lobes, 189; kinds of, 184–185; location of, 176–177; protein molecules in, 193–195; and recall, 138, 182–189; and sleep, 168; storage of, 6–7, 182, 188–195; and synapse, 140, 246; and temporal lobes, 185, 189–190; theoretical circuits of,

137–141, 188–193; and thinking, 178; *see also* computer(s); learning
meninges, 65
mental disease, 146–147, 253; in robots, 238
midbrain, 85, 86, 87, 115, 116; and autonomic nervous system, 123; and pineal body, 98; sleepwaking centers in, 171; and thalamus, 95
molecule(s), 109; role in memory, 193–195; as unit of protoplasm, 7
motivation, 144–145, 206
motor cortex, 101, 102, 103–104, 105–106; *see also* cortex
motor (efferent) neuron, 53, 75, 76, 77, 78–79; *see also* movement; nerve cell(s); sensorimotor circuit; sensory neuron
movement, 101–106; *see also* motor neuron; sensorimotor circuit
mutation, 22; *see also* inheritance
myelin sheath, 54, 55–56

natural selection, 22–23, 257, 258; *see also* artificial selection; evolution
Neanderthal man, 30, 36
nerve(s):
cranial, 50, 63–64, 85, 87, 90, 115–117; defined, 55, 58; peripheral, 56; spinal, 63, 64; *see also* nerve cell(s)
nerve cell(s):
axon and dendrites of, 54, 55; cell body of, 54, 55–57; of cerebral cortex, 100, 102–106; color of, 55; computer units compared to, 233, 244–245; interconnected, 137 ff., 198, 247; molecules of, 7, 193–195; of mouse, 4; myelin in, 54, 55–56; nucleus of, 54; neurilemma of, 54, 56, 57; number of, 3, 100; origin of, 43; regeneration of, 4, 57, 253; size of, 55; in thinking, 198–199; and trans-

Format by Robin Sherwood
Set in Linotype Electra
Composed by Brown Bros. Linotypers, Inc.
Printed by Rae Publishing Co.
Bound by Haddon Bindery
HARPER & ROW, PUBLISHERS, INCORPORATED